S0-BFC-849

Benefits of Herbs and Spices in Food

Vol. V.

Editor:
Thankam Mathew

Authors: Sandra F. El Hage & Thankam Mathew

----

31 Glen view Dr.
West Orange
NJ 07052 USA

E mail:thajema@ aol. com
Tel:973-731-6209
Fax:973-731-6209

Advances in Medical & Veterinary Virology, Immunology and Epidemiology

Benefits of Herbs and Spices in Food

Editor: Thankam Mathew
Authors: Sandra F. El Hage & Thankam Mathew

Series Editor: Thankam Mathew
Thajema Publishers
31 Glenview Drive
West Orange, NJ 07052-1010 USA
Tel/fax: 973-731-6209.
E. mail: <Thajema@aol.com>

The Benefits of Herbs and Spices in food

By

Sandra F. El Hage
Thankam Mathew

Publisher: Thankam Mathew, Managing Director, Thajema Publishers

The Benefits of Herbs and Spices in Food

Notice To The Reader

The publisher bears no liability resulting from the reader's use or reliance upon a part or the whole material presented in this book entitled: "Benefits of Herbs and Spices in food" by Sandra F. El Hage and Thankam Mathew.

Total pages: Text 134+Preliminary pages 18

Publishing Company Staff

Publisher: Thajema Publishers
Executive Editor: Dr. Thankam Mathew
Developmental Editor: Dr. Taji Susan Abraham
Project Editors: Dr. Tripthi Mary Mathew and Dr. Trini Ann Mathew
Computer setting and Proof reading: Mr. Bijou Abraham, Mr. Pradeep Kumar
Dr. Z. Mathew and Mrs. Audrey Chew and Miss. Kyle Tevlin
Copyright © 2005 Thajema Publishers

For information, contact:
Thajema Publishers,
31 Glenview Drive
West Orange, NJ 07052-1010 USA
Tel/fax: 973-731-6209
E.mail <Thajema@aol.com>
and also Sandra F. El Hage: <safe01@aub.edu.lb>

Printed in the United States of America.
At Book Masters, Inc. 2541 Ashland Road, P.O. Box 2139, Mansfield, Ohio 44905.

Cover Illustration: Provided by Mr. Nandakumar and Mrs. Nirmala Nandakumar. All the photos and pictures of the herbs and spices were taken and provided by Mr. Nandakumar and Mrs. Nirmala Nandakumar. Neighbors, Mr. Tim Stafford and Mrs. Sheila Tim who graciously contributed pictures of herbs / spices from their garden.

The Benefits of Herbs and Spices in Food
By
Sandra F. El Hage
&
Thankam Mathew

All rights reserved. All parts of this book are covered by the copy-right, and only the publisher has the privilege to issue written permission for reproduction of the material in the book in any form or by any means including: graphic, electronic, or mechanical. The mechanical means include: photocopying, recording, taping, or information storage and retrieval systems.

Copyright: ©Thajema 2005
Library of Congress: Cataloging – in–Publication Data
El Hage, Sandra, F.
Mathew, Thankam

Benefits of Herbs and Spices in food by
Sandra F. El Hage and Thankam Mathew

Includes bibliographical references and index.

ISBN 0-9727597-4-3
Title :Benefits of Herbs and Spices in food

Dedication

I, the first author, Sandra F. El Hage would like to dedicate this book
To my family
My father and mother Fawzi and Reine,
My two brothers Elias and Johnathan,
My two uncles Saad and Asaad.

I, the second author, Dr. Thankam Mathew like to dedicate this book to my late parents Mr. P.P. Devassy, Mrs. Mary Kattikaren , my late brother and siter-in-law Prof. Francis Thekkinyath and Thresiamma (Mini) Thekkinyath , my younger late brother Mr. Paul John Thekkinyath (Priyan) and my Botany professors and teachers , Mr. K. G. Krishna Rao, Mr. Raman, A., Mrs. Esther Hallegua and Prameswaren, C. A., who all created in me interest in herbs and spices.

Sandra F. El Hage   June 10th, 2004
      &
Thankam Mathew

Contents

Pages

Acknowledgment...ix-x
Preface...xi
About authors...xii-xiv
Picture of herbs and spices described in this book...................xv-xvi
Legends of pictures..xvii
Foreword of the book...xviii

Part A

Aniseed (*Pimpinella ansium*)   Chapter 1......1
Bay Leaf (*Laurus nobilis*)   Chapter 2......5
Black Pepper (*Piper Nigram*)   Chapter 3......9
Capsicum, Chillies(*Capsicum annum*)   Chapter 4.....13
Cardamom (*Ellectaria cardomomum*)   Chapter 5......17
Cinnamon (*Cinnamomum zeylanicum*)   Chapter 6......20
Clove (*Syzygium aromaticum*)   Chapter 7......24
Cumin (*Cuminum zyminum*)   Chapter 8......28
Curry leaf (*Murraya koenigii*)   Chapter 9......32
Dill (*Anethum graveolens*)   Chapter 10......36
Garlic (*Allium sativum*)   Chapter 11......39
Ginger (*Zingiber officinale*)   Chapter 12......44
Kokam and cambodge (*Garcinia indica*)   Chapter 13......48
Nutmeg and Mace (*Myristica fragrans*)   Chapter 14....53
Marjoram and Oregano (*Origanum majorana*)
                     (*Origanum vulgare*)   Chapter 15.....56
Onion (*Allium cepa*)   Chapter 16.....59
Rosmary and Sage (*Rosmarinus officinalis*) (*Salvia*)
                                                   Chapter 17.....64
Saffron (*Crocus sativus*)   Chapter 18.....68
Tamarind (*Tamarindus indica*)   Chapter 19.....71
Turmeric (*Cucurma domestica*)   Chapter 20.....74
Green tea (*Camellia sinensis*)   Chapter 21.....77
Licorice (*Glycyrrhiza glabra*)   Chapter 22.....83
Lavender (*Lavandula officinalis*)   Chapter 23.....87
Thyme (*Thymus vulgaris*)   Chapter 24......91

Part B Additional Chapters

Ajowan (*Caram Ajowan*)   Chapter 25.....95
Caraway seed (*Carum carvi*)   Chapter 25.....96
Basil (*Ocimum basilicum*)   Chapter 26.....98
Chamomile (*Matricaria chamomilla*)   Chapter 27....101
Coriander (*Coriandrum sativum*)   Chapter 28....104
Fennel (*Foeniculum vulgare*)   Chapter 29....106
Fenugreek (*Trigonella foenum-graecum*)   Chapter 30....108
Mint (*Menthae piperitae folium*)   Chapter 31....110
Mustard (*Brassica juncea*)   Chapter 32....112
Summary   114
References   115
Index   131

Acknowledgement:

I, Sandra F. El Hage would like to acknowledge all those people mentioned below who helped me and encouraged me in accomplishing this very first book of mine.

I will always be in their debt.

Dr Elie Barbour for his guidance at the times when I needed him, his enormous encouragement and generous help and support.

Dr Thankam Mathew for her cooperation, help and guidance to complete this first book of mine.

Dr Raja Tannous for his direction, devotion and patience.

Dr Omar Obeid for his help and support.

Dr Imad Toufeily for his honest critique of the book as well as his support.

My amazing parents Fawzi and Reine El-Hage to whom I want to express recognition and gratitude for everything they have ever done to me and still doing and whom I hope to honor. Thank you for always being next to me and supporting me in every step I choose to make.

My two brothers Elias and Johnathan El-Hage who supported and offered me help, patience, understanding and cooperation while writing this book. I am lucky to have such two amazing brothers.

My grandmother Najla for her encouragement and support.

My uncle Assad El-Hage for his precious support and encouragement from the very first moment.

My uncle Saad El-Hage whom, in spite of the long distance separating us, provided me with his support and pride.

Nesta for her support and guidance.

Georges for his help and moral support.

Last but not least, my dear friends Maya Zeitoun, Nadine Hasbani, Wilma Zakkour, Tarek, Joelle Seyouri and Lina for their encouragement.

The second author, Dr. Thankam Mathew is thankful to Sandra F. El Hage to create in me the enthusiasm to write and contribute many chapters in this book "Benefits of Herbs and Spices in Food", which will be of great advantage for human kind. I am also grateful to my husband Dr. Zachariah Mathew, for his encouragement and support in accomplishing my God given talent to continue writing and publishing books. Heartfelt thanks go also to my daughters Dr. Taji Susan Abraham, Dr Tripthi Mary Mathew and Dr. Trini Ann Mathew for all their support and healthy criticism while writing, editing and publishing the book. I am also thankful to Mr. Nandkumar and And Mrs. Nirmala Nandkumar for taking the photographs of the herbs and spices, which are included in this book and for the front cover page design of the book. Also grateful to Mr. Tim `Stafford and Mrs. Sheila Tim our neighbor who also provided photographs of some herbs which they are cultivating in their garden. I am grateful to Mr. Pradeep Kumar, who actually helped me in formatting and inserting the photographs in the appropriate places. A word of appreciation to my son-in- law Mr. Bijou Thomas Abraham and my brother- in- law Dr. Simon Zachariah for their computer expertise whenever I needed their help. I am grateful to Mrs. Audrey Chew for the proof reading of the book. Last but not least I want to thank all my friends who all have encouraged and helped me and God the Almighty who provided the talent and gave health to me to complete the book.

Sandra F. El Hage   June 10th 2004.
  &
Dr. Thankam Mathew

Preface:

What we aim to study in this book are herbs and spices that have always been present around us and in our meals. Have we however asked ourselves what is their nutritive value and their importance in our metabolism? Do they have a role or they are just used because that is how we cook?

Herbs and spices are valuable in adding flavor to foods. Their antioxidant activity preserves foods from oxidative deterioration, increasing their shelf life as well playing an important role as natural preservatives. For instance ground black pepper has been found to reduce the lipid oxidation of cooked pork. In addition, several antioxidants have been found isolated from spices and herbs: antioxidants play a role in the body's defense against cardiovascular disease and intestinal cancer (black pepper, oregano, thyme, and marjoram). Gingerol in ginger is also an intestinal stimulant and promoter of the bioactivity of drugs. Capsaicin in chilli pepper is an effective counter-irritant used in both pharmaceuticals and cosmetics. Finally onions, garlic and capsaicin help lower cholesterol level. A number of spices have also been identified as having anti microbial properties.

From another angle, they are beneficial in low-fat diets: instead of using vegetable oil or other fat substances such as margarines in cooking, we can use several kinds of spices and still be able to prepare a very tasteful variety of foods that will be low-caloric *i.e.*, low in their fat content and fat is the basic component related to obesity.

In this book, we will study each kind of spice and herb in a detailed way that will help us understand more and more the composition of our daily meals and more specifically the seasonings in them.

Sandra F. El Hage
&
Thankam Mathew

April 11th 2004.

About the authors

Sandra F. El Hage, B.Sc.

Therapeutic nutritionist
American University of Beirut
PO Box 11-236/260
Riad El-Solh 1107-2020
Beirut Lebanon
Fax: 961-1-744460
E-mail: Sandra_elhage@hotmail.com

She is a medical student who completed her B.Sc. degree in Nutrition and Dietetics at the American University of Beirut during her Studies in Medicine.

In addition to many articles and scientific papers such as "French fries and cancer", "Is sugar bad for us?" and "The inhibition of molds and yeast of pickled cucumbers by sunlight she is also writing a book this same year about "Frequently asked questions about food." that will be published soon, by 2005".

She presented some lectures and attended several conferences related to Obesity, Nutrition and Preventive Medicine.

In April 2004, she participated in the "Second National Congress in Daily Practice" entitled "Updates for General Practice" by presenting a conference about "Lebanese Diet in correlation to Obesity and Cardiovascular disease" at the Order of Medicine.

She is working as a clinical dietician, providing nutritional care and education to all those who believe that food is one of the major causes of illnesses and well-being, and that by good eating habits one can be able to reach the optimal good health.

Dr.Thankam Mathew, B.Sc., B.V.Sc., M.V.Sc.,

Ph.D., FISCD.

Consultant "Technomark" and Managing Director
Thajema Publishers
31 Glenview Drive
West Orange, NJ.07052 USA.
Tel/fax: 973-731-6209
E.mail:

Dr. Thankam Mathew was born in Ernakulam, State of Kerala, India. She passed the S.S.L.C. from St. Antony's High School, Pudukad and Bachelor of Science, B.Sc. in Botany (because of that she is interested in herbs and spices) from Maharajas college, Ernakulam. Her love and affection for the dumb and suffering animals, attracted her to study veterinary science and took her bachelors degree (B.V.Sc.) from Madras Veterinary College in the year 1958, with high credit and awards. She later became a lecturer at Kerala Veterinary College in Mannuthy, Trichur, as the first lady veterinarian to work in the State of Kerala. She took her postgraduate degree in Microbiology and Immunology from Madras Veterinary College in the year 1962. ICAR awarded her a Senior Research Fellowship in the subject of Virology leading to her Ph.D. degree in 1967. She was the receipient of the Diamond Jubilee Post Doctoral Fellowship of Haffkine Institute in Bombay, where she received her Ph.D. and also worked as a CSIR Pool officer (scientist) assignment till 1971, working on Antilymphocyte serum as an immuno-suppressor and also on some immuno-enhancers. Since then she has worked as a Senior Research Officer of the Indian Council of Medical Research (ICMR) Virus unit, at Stanley Medical College Madras and the National Institute of Communicable Disease Delhi, until 1979. Later she worked as the Principal Scientific Officer and Head of the Veterinary Public Health Laboratory, Federal Livestock Department, Kaduna, Nigeria, until 1983. After her return from Nigeria , she took up the Senior Research Associate Fellowship of the ICMR and worked on "Basic research on the pathogenic mechanism of diarrhea by different bacterial agents and genetic studies on enterogenic plasmids *etc.*", at Maulana Azad Medical College, New Delhi, until October 31,1984.

Later she established a diagnostic laboratory "Thankam Laboratories", for diseases diagnosis for human, animal and poultry and worked as Director of the laboratory, until 1993 when she migrated to the USA. While working in the laboratory, she also worked as Managing Director of Thajema Publishers and published two books and the *Bulletin of Indian Association of Lady Veterinarians*. After coming to the USA, as a permanent resident, she worked as Manager of the Quality Control Laboratory at IGI Inc., Vineland for poultry vaccine production. Later, she concentrated on book publishing work and became a U.S. Citizen, established Thajema Publishing and continued the series publication of the book *Advances in Medical & Veterinary Virology, Immunology and Epidemiology.* The book Vol.3 *Modern Concepts of Immunology in Veterinary Science-Poultry Immunology* was released in 2002.The book Vol. 4 of the series *Zoonoses and the contribution of Disease-free Pets to human Health: A guide to pet owners* was released by July 2004. She has 90 scientific papers to her credit in addition to the four books published in 1987, 1993, 2002 and 2004 and a few scientific booklets. Dr. T. Mathew had different awards from universities and from different associations for her credit in various subjects and activities. She has also presented scientific papers and posters during the various National and International Conferences in India, Nigeria, Germany, USA, Australia, France, Canada, and Brazil. She is the Founder Secretary and was President of the Indian Association of Lady Veterinarians and a member of World Women Veterinarians. Presently, she is a member of the American Association of Women Veterinarians and also had been a member of various international organizations.

Pictures of Herbs and Spices Described in this book

Fig 1

Fig 2

Fig 3

Fig 4

Fig 5

Fig 6

Fig 7

Fig 8

Fig 9

Fig 10

Fig 11

Fig 12

Fig 13

Fig 14

Fig 15

Fig 16

Fig 17

Fig 18

Fig 19   Fig 20   Fig 21

Fig 22   Fig 23   Fig 24

Fig 25   Fig 26   Fig 27

Fig 28   Fig 29   Fig 30

Fig 31   Fig 32   Fig 33

Legends of Pictures

Fig. No. Name of herbs   **Page No. in the text**

Fig. 1. Aniseed..Page 1.
Fig. 2. Bay leaf.. Page 5.
Fig. 3. Black Pepper............................... Page 9.
Fig. 4. Capsicum, Chilies.......................Page 13.
Fig. 5. Cardamom..................................Page 17.
Fig. 6. Cinnamon...................................Page 20.
Fig. 7. Clove..Page 24.
Fig. 8. Cumin...Page 28.
Fig. 9. Curry leaf...................................Page 32.
Fig.10. Dill...Page 36.
Fig.11. Garlic ....Page 39.
Fig.12. Ginger..Page 44.
Fig.13. Kokam.......................................Page 48.
Fig.14. Mace..Page 52.
Fig.15. Marjoram ....Page 55.
Fig.16. Oregano.....................................Page 55.
Fig.17. Onion...Page 58.
Fig.18. Rosmary ....Page 63.
Fig.19. Saffron.......................................Page 67.
Fig.20. Tamarind ....Page 70.
Fig.21. Turmeric....................................Page 73.
Fig.22. Green Tea...................................Page 76.
Fig.23. Licorice......................................Page 82.
Fig.24. Lavender....................................Page 86.
Fig.25. Thyme..Page 90.
Fig.26. Ajowan......................................Page 95.
Fig.27. Basil...Page 98.
Fig.28. Chamomile.................................Page 101.
Fig.29. Coriander...................................Page 104.
Fig.30. Fennel..Page 106.
Fig.31. Fenugreek...................................Page 108.
Fig.32. Mint..Page 110.
Fig.33. Mustard......................................Page 112.

FOREWORD

The authors have bestowed on me the honour of writing a foreword to their learned study on The Benefit of Herbs And Spices in Food. As an ayurvedic physician I live in the world of herbs and anything related to them is of great joy to me.

Ayurveda prescribes a strict regimen of life for longevity. Food is considered as the first protector of life. The body itself has come into being from food. When food is nutritious, body gets the full benefit of it. The food becomes nourishing when the six *rasas* contained in food materials – sweet, sour, salt, acrid, bitter and astringent – are properly digested and absorbed. Herein comes the role of herbs and spices. They add flavour, act as stimulants interacting with taste-buds and kindle the fire (*agni*) within. They also defend the body from the attack of diseases *i.e.* prevent cholesterol buildup, ease digestive disorders and take up the function of anti-oxidants.

This work gives the details of 36 important herbs and spices with their scientific names, habitat, chemical structure, uses in food processing, the medical and functional properties, *etc.* The authors have collected all available data and arranged them with scientific precision.

Apart from the bare facts, the authors present interesting anecdotes, traditional beliefs and religious importance of herbs in different parts of the world. We come to know that the bay leaves in biblical times represented wealth and that they were offered as rewards to the winners in Olympic games; that the Arabs mixed cardamom to their coffee believing that it was aphrodisiac stimulating the libido and nervous system; that Chinese sweetened their breath with clove before talking to their emperor; that cumin symbolized greed to the Greeks and they jocularly said of misers having eaten cumin, and that turmeric, known as the salt of the orient, was used in wedding ceremonies in Java. These and similar descriptions make the reading of this book more interesting.

I am sure that this work will be of great use not only to the scientific world, but also to the clinical dieticians, housewives, heath-care promoters and general public.

Arya Vaidya Sala, Kottakkal   Dr. P.K. Warrier
Kerala, India
20.12.2004   Managing Trustee & Chief Physician

Chapter 1
Aniseed : English
Jeerakam: (Malayalam)
Jeera: (Hindi)

Introduction:

Scientific Name: *Pimpinella anisum*
Source: *Pimpinella anisum* L. (Syn. *Anisum vulgare* Gaertn; *Anisum officinarum* Monch; *Apium anisum* (L.) Crantz; *Carum anisum* (L.) Baill; *Selinum anisum* (L.) E.H.L. Krause; *pimpinella anisum* (var.) cultum Alef; *Sison anison* Spreng; *Tragium anisum* (link).
Family Name: *Apiaceae* (= *Umbelliferae*)
Synonyms: Aniseed, Anis seed, Anis, Anise, Sweet cumin
Parts used: Seeds (fruits), oil (Duke, 1997).

Aniseed is grown in Egypt and the East Mediterranean and is now cultivated in many countries, namely, Turkey, Egypt, Spain, Russia, Italy, India, Greece, Northern-Africa, Argentina, Malta, Romania, and Syria. Anise requires a warm and long frost-free growing season of 120 days. The plant needs a hot summer to thrive and for the seeds to ripen. It develops well in deep, rich, well-drained, sandy and calcareous soils. Ripe-fruits' seeds germinate quickly. The optimal soil for its germination is 18-21 degrees Celsius. After the germination, the plant develops slowly. Anise seeds are harvested between the end of July and the beginning of September (Elisabeth, 1992). Concerning the plant itself, its root is thin and spindle-shaped, the stem up, stalk round, grooved and branched upward. In mid-summer, the thin stems are topped with tiny white flowers that turn into seed-like fruits. Commercially available aniseed usually contains the whole fruits and occasionally parts of the fruitstalk. The fruits are downy, and their color is grayish-green to grayish-brown.

Habitat:
Aniseed prefers warm, sunny, rich, sandy soil and well-drained areas. North America has an abundance of this annual plant with the height of 1-2 feet. It needs 120 days to produce fully-ripened seed heads.

Religious Importance:

It is believed that if anise is blended with bay leaves, it provides an excellent bath additive prior to ritual. Anise grown around the home keeps off evil and if it is placed in the sleeping pillow at night, it chases away nightmares. Also, in most parts of the world, anise seed head is hung on the bed post to restore youth (Elisabeth, 1992).

Chemical Structure:

Anise contains:

1-4% volatile oil

Coumarins bergapten, umbelliprenine, umbelliferone, scopoletin.

ca. 8-16% lipids, including fatty-acids: 50-70% petroselinic acid (C18:1), 22-28% oleic acid (C18:1), 5-9% linoleic acid (C18:2) and 5-10% saturated fatty acids, mostly palmitic acid (C16:0).

β- amyrin, and stigmasterol and its salts (palmitate and stearate)

Flavonoids glycosides: quercetin-3-glucoronide, rutin, luteolin-7-glucoside, isoorientin, isovitexin, apigenin-7-glucoside (apigetrin), *etc.*

Myristicin

ca. 18% protein.

ca. 50% carbohydrate and other (Peter, 2001).

Anethole: Compound similar to female sex hormone estrogen.

Main Uses in Food Processing:

Aniseed was not discovered recently. It got its popularity from its main uses: culinary, household, cosmetic and medicinal. Aniseed is one of the oldest spices used for flavoring curries, breads, Italian sausage, pepperoni, pizzas, soups, and baked goods such as German springerle, Italian biscotti and Arabic kaak. It is also used for sweets, dry figs, pickles and non-alcoholic beverages (Arabian arak, vodka). All parts of the plant are used (not only the seeds that we call aniseed). For instance, the flowers and the leaves can be added to fruit salads and the roots and the stems give just a hint of licorice (Duke, 1997).

The essential oil is used for perfumery, in dentifrice as antiseptic, soaps, detergents, lotions and skin creams. Finally, the oil is used for the production of anethole and sometimes as sensitizer for bleaching colors in photography (Peter, 2001).

Medicinal and Functional Properties:

The pharmaceutical data mentioned refer mainly to the anise oil and anethole. Anethole is structurally related to catecholamines adrenaline, noradrenaline and dopamine. Anise oil and anethole have several properties such as:

antibacterial, antifungal, antioxidant, stimulant, carminative and expectorant.

The antibacterial activities of the essential oil from *Pimpinella anisum* were found effective against *Staphylococcus aureus, Streptococcus pyrogens, Escherichia* and *Corynebacterium ovis* (Peter, 2001).

Anethole, as a part of the volatile oil from aniseed, has been identified as having a significant antifungal activity (Duke, 1997) against members of the genera *Alternaria, Aspergillus, Cladosporium, Fusarium* and *Penicillium.* Additional roles of anethole are that it inhibits the growth of mycotoxin producing aspergillus in species and is mutagenic in Ames *Salmonella* reversion assay. There is some evidence of anise oil's effectiveness as an antioxidant and that are better than that of a synthetic antioxidant such as butylated hydroxytoluene (Peter, 2001).

Anise oil is used as a carminative, stimulant, mild spasmolytic, weak antibacterial agent and as an expectorant in cough mixtures and lozenges (Duke, 1997). It can be used internally for dyspeptic complaints and externally as an inhalant for congestion of the respiratory tract. Also it can be used by boiling the seeds in water and drinking one or two cups of the water everyday to reduce or heal bronchial congestion (Duke, 1997).

In addition, anise has a lot of other health benefits, such as promoting iron absorption in the body, stimulating hepatic regeneration, decreasing aggression and preventing the reduction in milk production in dairy cattle (Peter, 2001).

In traditional medicine, anise is used as an aromatic carminative, a stimulant and an expectorant. It is also used as an oestrogenic agents to increase milk production, promote menstruation, facilitate birth, increase libido and alleviate symptoms of male climacteric-change of life (Duke, 1997). The oil itself may be helpful in the control of lice, bronchial complaints, skin parasites and as a chest rub. The seeds have been used to freshen bad breath. In addition, by boiling the anise plant in water for few minutes we will get a drinkable mixture that can be used for a mouth wash (Duke, 1997). Aniseed prevents nausea and helps in digestion. It also acts as an aphrodisiac (Ellen, 1997).

Toxicity and Allergy:

In general, anise and oil of anise are considered safe for human consumption. Aniseed contains anethole and estragole, which are structurally related to safrole, a known hepatotoxin and carcinogen. Anethole has two isomers (*cis* and *trans)*. The *cis* isomer is 18-35 times more toxic to animals than trans. The major component of the natural anise oil (80-96%), is trans-anethole which is more likely non-carcinogenic.

Aniseed may cause an allergic reaction. It is recommended that the use of anise oil should be avoided in dermatitis, or any inflammatory or allergic skin condition. When consumed in sufficient quantities, anise oil may cause nausea, vomiting, seizures and pulmonary edema. As for the direct contact of concentrated oil of anise, it has been proved to cause irritations. Finally, anethole has been reported to cause dermatitis (erythema, scaling and vesiculation) (Peter, 2001).

Chapter 2
Bay Leaves :*English*
Karuva Ela: (Malayalam)
Tejpetta :(Hindi)

Introduction:

Scientific Name: *Laurus nobilis*
Family Name :*Lauraceae*

The commodity, traded as sweet bay leaf, and true, Roman, or Turkish laurel is derived from the leaves of *Laurus nobilis L.* derived from the *Lauraceae* family (Cecil, 1998).

It has many synonyms such as: Sweet Bay Laurel, Grecian Laurel, True Bay and Mediterranean Bay (D'Amelio,1999).

The leaves of the true *L. nobilis* must not be confused with other laurels (Portugal laurel, cherry laurel).

This plant is widely cultivated in Mediterranean countries (D'Amelio, 1999) and grows unexpectedly in scrubland and woods in Europe and America and in Arabian countries from Libya to Morocco (Matsuda *et al.*, 2000).

The flavoring properties of *L. nobilis* have been known since the ancient times. In addition to this, its leaves and fruits are used everywhere around the world. They are added to several stews as well as used as herbal medicines for stimulant, stomachic and digestive purposes (Afifi *et al.*, 1997). It is also applicable in veterinary medicine. The bay tree is an evergreen shrub attaining a height of 15-20 m. The bark is smooth and may have an olive green or reddish color. The flowers are small, yellow in color and appear in clusters; they are cultivated in autumn. The fruits are cherry-like, ovoid and succulent. The used parts are the leaves and the fruits. The bay trees are cultivated in the summer.

The leaf has a distinguishing fragrance when crushed and possesses an aromatic and bitter taste. Bay leaves have to be sun dried before using for culinary purposes, especially by French people (Peter, 2001). Steam distillation can isolate the essential aromatic oil as well as the spicy odor and flavor. This kind of oil can be used in meats, sausages, canned soups, baked goods and confectionery.

Religious importance:

In biblical times, bay leaves symbolized wealth and wickedness (Duke, 1983). In the ancient times this tree used to be called Apollo's bay and it was used to treat coughs and hysteria attacks. But in the ancient Olympic Games, a chaplet of bay leaves was offered as a reward for the winner; they used to place it on his brow. Moreover, the Romans had a laurel wreath on the gold coin of 342 B.C.

Chemistry:

Bay leaves basically contain α-pinene, eugenol, free alcohols, terpene hydrocarbons, carbonyl compounds (11.48%), 1-8 cineole (35%), limonene, methyl eugenol and α-phellandrene (Masayuki *et al.*, 2000).The plant contains alkaloids, catechins and plant acids as well (D'Amelio, 1999).

Four types of sesquiterpenes can be isolated from the ethyl acetate soluble part of the laurus plant: the first type is the Germacrane, such as the costunolide; the second one is the guinane-type, including dehydrocostus lactone and zaluzanin D; the third type is the eudesmane (Farouk and Dantel, 1983), such as santamarine (Romo, 1965), reynosin, eudesmol and finally the last sesquiterpene is the caryophyllene-type, including the caryophyllene oxide.

Medicinal and Functional properties:

Sweet Bay is a very familiar domestic spice known as bay leaves. Its oil is mainly used as a fragrance in creams and lotions.
Perfumes: The evergreen leaves, when broken, emit a sweet scent and furnish an extract that is used in the perfume making. It is also used in soaps, made from the fat of the fruits (Duke, 1985) and as detergents (D'Amelio, 1999).

Dried bay leaves are used to flavor many food items such as meats, fishes and poultry, vegetables, soups and stews.
It is also used in pickling processes, such as spices and vinegar.

Bay leaves are specifically used in French cuisine and platters.
The leaves, at their turn, serve as a tea substitute or they can be used as well with coffee.
An essential oil that is obtained after distillation of bay leaves is used in the flavoring of several food items such as baked goods, confectionery, meat, sausages and canned meat.

The bay leaf oil has been widely used in traditional medicine for the treatment of diseases and sickness.
It has many properties such as:
    Antimicrobial and antifungal characteristics;
    Hypoglycemic properties (in the control of diabetes);
    Antiulcerogenic properties.

The essential oil has been found effective against *Staphylococcus aureus, Salmonella typhi, Escherichia coli* and *Shigella flexnerii,* bacteria of the intestinal tract. The anti-fungal activity of bay leaves has been identified in many research studies.

As for the hypoglycemic property, bay leaves potential the action of insulin in glucose metabolism and reduce glucose transport, therefore helping diabetic people (Afifi *et al.,* 1997). Bay leaves help the body to use insulin effectively; they help to lower the blood glucose level and therefore should be used by diabetic people. (Wada *et al.,* 1997). Duke (1997) reported that the bay leaf lowers blood sugar in both experimental animals and humans.

Many other properties of bay leaves were reported due to the high absorption which will lead to blood ethanol elevation, cockroach repellant activity-used in pesticides, retardation of gastric emptying and antioxidant properties.
Due to the presence of a compound known as parthenolides, *Laurus nobilis* is used in preventing migraines. Migraines appear due to the release of neurotransmitters such as serotonin from the blood platelets, what the bay leaves do is that they inhibit the serotonin release from the platelets, therefore preventing severe headaches (Antoine, 1998).
Bay contains 1,8-cineole, which is a powerful bacteria killer found in its aromatic oil and used in toothpastes. Its main function is preventing tooth decay (Duke, 1997).

bay leaves can be used as deodorants since they possess the antibacterial action that acts against the microorganism producing apocrine secretion leading to bad smells.

In traditional treatments, bay leaf was used as an aperitif, carminative, diuretic, emetic, emmenagogue, narcotic, nervine stimulant, especially against back pain and joints (Antoine, 1998), stomachic and sudorific. (Duke, 1985). The bay leaf lower the sugar in experimental animals (Duke, 1997).

Toxicity and allergenicity:
Bay leaves and their derived essential oil have not been found to have any relevant toxicity; however they may lead to some allergies, such as dermatitis, stomatitis and cheilitis, or gastrointestinal disease leading to the accumulation of *Clostridium perfringens* spores (Peter, 2001).

Chapter 3

Black Pepper: (English)
Kurumulaku :(Malayalam)
Kali Mirchi :(Hindi)

Introduction:

Scientific Name: *Piper nigrum*
Family Name : *Piperacae*
Genus: *Piper*

Among all spices, black pepper is the "best", and is called the "King of Spices." Peppercorns are given for bride's dowries and rent and is named as Peppercorn Rent (Ellen, 1997). It is the most important spice and the most commonly used.

Southwest India, Malabar Cost, is the traditional home of this important spice. But nowadays it can be found in many tropical zones, such as Indonesia, Malaysia, Sri lanka, China, Vietnam, Cambodia and Brazil. It is known in India by different names, as "Kalimirchi" in the Hindi language and "Kurumulaku" in Malayalam. In Sanskrit, Pipper is known as Pipplle nigrum, and Pipper nigrum came from the Sanskrit name.

In search of this spice, people from the west were trying to go to India, but landed in the USA and discovered America (Ellen,1997). Black pepper is collected from the mature fruits of *Piper nigrum L.*, a perennial climbing evergreen, rooting at the nodes. Though pepper is known to be a tropical plant requiring a hot humid climate, it can tolerate many types of environmental conditions, such as high rainfall and uniform temperature. The best soil types recommended for the cultivation of the black pepper plant are deep, well-drained brownish red latosols or andosols. The crop can grow in sandy clay as well, on the condition that it is provided with mineral nutrition and adequate drainage.

Chemical structure:

Pepper is made up of two general constituents, which are:
Piperine $C_{17}H_{19}O_3N$ (a weak base and a major alkaloid present in pepper) that is related to the pungency, and volatile oil, which is responsible for the aroma and the flavor. The oil is a mixture of a large number of volatile chemical compounds such as:
Monoterpene hydrocarbons and oxygenated compounds;
Sesquiterpene hydrocarbons and oxygenated compounds *i.e.* caryophyllene;
Miscellaneous compounds *i.e.* eugenol, methyl eugenol, benzaldehyde, safrole, pinol, n-butyrophenone.

Oleoresin of black pepper, which is produced by solvent extraction of dried powdered pepper, contains both factors. In addition, we have the phenolic components of pepper that are a combination of the glycosides of phenolic acids and flavonol glycosides. Finally, sisterol is an additional pepper component.

Nutritional value:

Per 100 grams of black pepper fruit, there are 255 calories, 11 grams of protein, 3.3 grams of fat, 68.5 grams of carbohydrate, 13.1 grams of fiber, and 4.3 grams of ash.
In addition, pepper contains several minerals such as: calcium, potassium, sodium, iron and phosphorous.
As for vitamins, black pepper includes thiamine, riboflavin and niacin (Duke, 1985).

Kinds of pepper:

The importance of pepper has been recognized since ancient times.
There are several kinds of pepper:
 First of all, we have white pepper, that is mainly found in food items that should be a light in color, such as in some soups, mayonnaise, and light colored sauces. It is prepared from fully ripe fruit by removing the pericarp, the outer layer, before drying.

Then we have ground pepper, which is the most common form of pepper used in almost all kinds of food and it is created by grinding white and black pepper together. Nowadays they do this by cryogrinding, which is nothing but a grinding done at a low temperature in order to reduce the oil loss; it is done by injecting liquid nitrogen into the grinding zone.

Finally, we have **pepper oil** and **olestrin,** which are mainly utilized as spice drops (Peter, 2001).

Use of pepper in food:
Pepper is used in cooking for several purposes, such as:
Flavoring, masking/deodorizing, for pungency, and as a colorant.

Pepper interacts with the taste buds, leading to complex effects. It is used in both vegetarian and non-vegetarian foods. It is suitable for eggs, meat, seafood, milk, grain and vegetables. It is also used in the preparation of curry powder, the famous Five Spice Blend (used in almost all dishes around the world), as well as in several beverages (pepper tea, pepper milk shake), snacks (Pongal, Bonda, vegetable crispies), soups (cream of vegetable soup), meat dishes (pepper steak, korma curry, pepper mutton balls) and sweets (Soji Halwa, quick banana pudding).

Medicinal and functional properties
Pepper has been found to possess several functions, such as:
analgestic, and antipyretic, and antioxidant properties.

Antioxidant effects in pepper are related to the flavonoids present in it, such as: quercetin, luteolin, capsaicin, and ascorbic acid. Lee *et al.,* (1995) showed the effect of pepper on lipid peroxidation.

After boiling, pepper retains its antioxidant properties and even more, it shows high antioxidant activities, which shows that the spice constituents are resistant to thermal denaturation (Gazzani, 1994).

Pepper is used for flavoring and preservation, and is important medicinally, as well. Used in medicine, it serves as a carminative, febrifuge, diuretic, aid in digestion and cure for the common cold. It is also used for arthritis, asthma, fever, cough, dysentery, flatulence and hemorrhoids. It has antimicrobial properties against *Vibrio cholerae, Staphylococcus albus, Clostridium diphthereae, Shigella dysenteriae, Streptomyces faecalis, Bacillus sp. and Pseudomonas.*

It was discovered that piperine reduces inflammation simply by being absorbed through the skin, having the capacity to act on the subcutaneous tissues as well as on the nerves and blood vessels, such as for lowering blood pressure (Duke, 1997).

The effect of pepper on the nervous system and sexual organs indicates anticonvulsive and vasodilatory properties.

More than this, pepper has been found to contain four antiosteoporosis constituents (Duke, 1997).

In addition, pepper was found to have an effect on lactation, by increasing milk production due to its action on mammary glands, and against electroshock seizure and epilepsy, as its oil warms the skin and brings blood to the surface, there by this stimulating circulation (Peter, 2001).

Finally, both pepper and piperine have liver-protection action, and pepper leaf oil has antifungal activity.

Pepper can be used for constipation, flatulence, diarrhea, colic and headaches. It can also be used as an insecticide and prevent moths on cloth or fabric.

Chapter 4
Capsicum, chilies, paprika: *(English)*
Mulaku : (Malayalam)
Lal Mirchi : (Hindi)

Introduction:

Scientific Name: *Capsicum annum,*
                    C. bacctatum
Family Name : *Solanaceae*
Genus : *Capsicum*

The genus Capsicum is widely grown and is known for its different fruits which may be eaten fresh, or dried and used as powders or in sauces, or processed into oleoresin. There exists three major products for this genus: paprika, oleoresin, and dried chili.

The genus capsicum belongs to the family Solanaceae, which is divided into five species: *Capsicum annum, C. baccatum, C. chinense, C. frutescens,* and *C. pubescens.* The classification system for this genus is confusing; in Spain, they name any Capsicum specie by 'pimiento', whereas in the USA 'pimiento' is only used for the thick-walled, heart-shaped, non-pungent fruit from the *Capsicum annum* species. Hungarians call the *Capsicum annum* "paprika," known in the world market as a ground red powder derived from dried fruit. In Asia, the word 'chili' is associated with highly pungent varieties of *Capsicum annum* and *C. pubescens,* while the non-pungent sweet bell peppers are referred to as 'capsicum' (Peter, 2001).

Peter (2001) tried to explain the difference between the different kinds: Oleoresin is a liquid derived by solvent extraction from ground powder of any capsicum species, and there are three types: paprika (used for its color), red pepper (used for its color and pungency) and capsicum (used only for its pungency).

Paprika is a bright red ground (its color is not as stable as oleoresin and capsicum), and all paprika are *Capsicum annum* Paprika fruits are used for paprika oleoresin.

Chili is an overpowering of any capsicum variety, but especially *Capsicum annum,* which is used to produce red pepper oleoresin or capsicum oleoresin.

Pepper is the generic term describing the fruits of any capsicum species, pungent or not.

Peppers are used as colorants, flavorings and as a source of pungency. An alkaloid compound known as capsaicinoids (CAPS), produced in the fruit, is the major source of pungency in this plant.

The most abundant CAPS is the capsaicin ($C_{18}H_{27}NO_3$, trans-8-methyl-N-vanillyl-6-noneamide), which is a white crystalline, fat-soluble solution compound formed from homovanillic acid that is odorless and tasteless (Peter, 2001). Capsicum is insoluble in cold water and only slightly soluble in hot water (Vogl, 1982).

In Peru, *C. pubescens* is also used to punish children by making them hold the burning chilies, and if young girls gaze at or look on any handsome man for some time, they are punished by rubbing chilies into their eyes (Ellen, 1997).

Main uses in food processing:

There are many uses of paprika in food processing:
a. Color: People use pepper to add some lively color to their everyday dishes. Paprika, paprika oleoresin, red pepper oleoresin, and dried chili all equally provide this desired red color in various food products, but paprika and paprika oleoresin are the main ones. Paprika is used when there should be no pungency, such as in cheeses (*e.g.* Rambol), sausages, soups (*e.g.* Chinese soups), sauces, and snacks such as potato chips, where paprika oleoresin is used because paprika's small particles of powder are undesirable. Paprika is extensively used in Indian and Chinese cooking.
b. Pungency: Red pepper oleoresin is used in soups, sandwich spreads and smoked pork. Capsicum oleoresin has advantages over dried chili, including more stable color and pungencies values.

c. Flavor: Paprika and dried chili are both used in foods because of their flavoring principle, which is related to volatile aromatic compounds and color. Flavor and color are interrelated, thus when the color of one fades away, its flavor fades, too.

d. Pharmaceutical: Capsicum oleoresin is the main form of pepper used for pharmaceutical properties. At least two pain relief products are used in the market, and they are: creams containing 0.75 % capsaicin *i.e.* Zostrix, and plasters containing 3% oleoresin *i.e.*Vorwerk. Several types of capsules contain chili powder (cayenne powder) with a range of capsaicin are being marketed (Peter, 2001).

Functional properties:
As Peter (2001) explained, CAPS excite sensory neurons in the skin and mouth cavity, creating a sensation of warmth that will increase to severe pain with higher doses. The neurons produce the neuropeptide substance P (SP), which delivers the message to pain. Repeated exposure to capsicum depletes SP, and thereby eliminates the feeling of pain in many people.

Peppers have been reported to contain an anticoagulant that helps in preventing the formation of blood clots that may lead to heart attacks and blockage of the arteries.

A meal containing CAPS increases the thermic effect of foods for up to 25% for three hours, which leads to more burned calories. In addition, it was found that the more CAPS a person consumes, the more endorphins the body releases, therefore causing a person to feel naturally high, *i.e.* mild euphoria (Peter, 2001).

Capsicum has many other functional properties, such as:
Stomachic, carminative, and gastrointestinal stimulants (Locock, 1985).
Acting as a counterirritant, capsicum is a rubefacient, (Locock, 1985) and has a long lasting action and does not blister the skin (Sollmann, 1948).
Reducing blood cholesterol level (Visudhiphan *et al.*, 1982).
Decreasing blood clotting (Castleman, 1989).
Circulatory stimulant.

Decreasing cluster headaches.
Preventing herpes and ulcers, curing shingles (Ellen, 1997).
Treating dry mouth.
Treating shingles (Duke, 1997).
Acting as an antiseptic (D'Amelio, 1999).
Increasing body temperature when needed in cold weather.
Helping to reduce cramps and paralysis (Ellen, 1997).

Nowadays, capsicum is being used as an ointment for treating chronic pain due to herpes zoster, trigeminal neuralgia and surgical trauma, stump pain following an amputation.

Most of capsicum's activities are due to its capsaicin content, which is responsible for the pungency of the fruit.

Capsicum is considered as a good source of vitamins A, E and potassium (Foster, 1999).

Finally, capsicum is used in hair tonics to stimulate the follicle along with nettles and colocynth (D'Amelio, 1999).

Toxicity:

Toxicity of CAPS as a food additive has been found negligible in humans. However, if the quantity of capsicum used is relatively high, it might be very irritating and upsetting for the eyes as well as the digestive system.

A person must be very careful when using hot peppers, because traces remaining on the hands, for instance, may be transferred inadvertently to sensitive mucous membranes, even several hours after contact (Vogl, 1982).

If under any circumstances, an organ of your body becomes irritated by hot peppers, the best way to handle the situation is to bathe your affected part in vinegar. This should not be applied for inside or around the eyes.

Capsicum products should be kept away from children.

Chapter 5

Cardamom: English
Elakka : (Malayalam)
Ealichi : (Hindi)

Introduction:
Scientific Name: *Electtaria cardamomum*
Family Name: *Zingiberaceae*

Several varieties of seed plants are known as cardamom, but the best known are the ones exported from India, where they are extracted from a ginger-like plant.

Cardamom comes from a plant that is in the ginger family. Cardamom is the dried seed capsule of a small group of species of plants belonging to the *Zingiberaceae* family.
Its seeds possess an aromatic, pleasant taste and smell.
There are two kinds of cardamom:
> small cardamom, known as "chhota Elaichi" in Hindi
> large cardamom, known as Bada Elaichi in Hindi

Dried large cardamom capsules are on average 25 mm long, oval to globose; grayish brown to dark red brown (Peter, 2001). The fruit of large cardamom are bigger than those of the true cardamom, however their seeds are of the same size.
Cardamom is an expensive spice that can be a mild stimulant.

Habitat:
Cardamom seeds grow wild in the rainforests of India. It is the third most expensive spice in the world.
Cardamom is cultivated in India, Sri Lanka, Cambodia, Guatemala and El-Salvador.

Religious importance and folklore:
As cited by the heartsong chai, "Since centuries, Arabs used to utilize cardamom in their coffee in a belief that it was aphrodisiac. They think

that it stimulates the libido and the nervous system. It was used traditionally to rid unwanted thoughts and calm physical stress."
"The ancient Vedic texts of medicine mention cardamom. The Vedic traditions of India began over 1000 years before Christ Jesus was born. According to Indian people, cardamom can be used along with milk and honey to fight depression".

"Ancient Egyptians chewed cardamom seeds as a tooth cleaner. Greece was importing cardamom since the fourth century. Greeks and Romans used it as perfume. It was the Romans who were responsible for making cardamom popular. Cardamom traveled to Europe through the old caravan routes. European healers first documented its beneficial properties in herbal books of the Renaissance period" (Elisabeth, 1992).

Chemical structure:
The composition varies among regions and age of the product, the average being of 70% seeds and 30% skin. Large cardamom contains moisture, ash, protein, crude fiber, alcohol extract and starch. The volatile oil present in the seeds is responsible for providing the typical odor and aroma which is described as a comphory, sweet, aromatic spice. Volatile oil from cardamom contains few hydrocarbons and a large amount of 1, 8-cineole and α-cineole and α-terpinyl acetate.

Main use:
This herb enhances both sweet and savory flavors. It is used in a number of sweet and spice mixtures.
Cardamom is used for:
1. Flavoring various vegetables, soups and meat products;
2. Adding to herbal tea and liquors;
3. Flavoring agents in confectionery and pickles;
4. Easing cigarette addiction;
5. Spice mixtures, perfumery and liquor preparation and in the pharmaceutical industries;
6. Reviving people who have fainted, bringing them back to consciousness (Duke, 1997);
7. Its curative properties in the unani and ayurvedic systems of medicine (Peter, 2001).

Medicinal and functional properties:

Cardamom is used for its cooling effects on the body, as well as for skin disorders, piles, jaundice, headaches, and fever. It also aides in weight loss and can be used as a sliming aid (Ellen, 1997).

Cardamom can be used as a temporary relief from the symptoms of catarrh and coughs. It is also used to treat the discomfort caused by gastritis and stomach disorders.

Cardamom has many other functions, such as:

Use as an adjuvant to carminative drugs and as an aromatic stimulant;

A very rich source of cineole, which acts as an antiseptic to kill bad breath's bacteria. It is breath-freshening when chewed;

The cineole present in it acts as an expectorant, in fighting emphysema for instance;

Use as an anti-asthmatic herb (Duke, 1997);

Use as an aphrodisiac, treating impotence;

Stimulating the appetite;

Alleviating the bad breath;

Treating vaginitis;

Treating fevers;

Treating inflammatory conditions of the oropharynx and liver disorders;

An important aid in digestion;

Treating digestive problems and helping to eliminate gas (D'Amelio, 1999);

Use in many pharmaceutical preparations (Warrier *et al.,* 1994).

Toxicity:

Cardamom should not be used by children; it is only recommended for adults (Norman, 1990).

Chapter 6

Cinnamon: *(English)*
Karuva Patta : (Malayalam)
Dalcini : (Hindi)

Introduction:
Scientific Name: *Cinnamomum zeylanicum, aromaticum.*
Family Name: *Laureacea.*

Cinnamon is nothing but the bark of an evergreen plant.
It is known as canella in French, ceylonzeimt / kaneel in German, canella in Italian and dal-chini in Hindi. Cinnamon is obtained by drying the central part of the bark.
True cinnamon has a single spiral curl and is almost papery, brittle, and easily crushed or bruised.
Its flavor is somewhat subdued, not bitter. It has a sweet, aromatic taste.
Cinnamon should be stored in a dry, cool place. The aromatic oils of this plant will dissipate if exposed to high temperature and humidity.

Habitat:
Cinnamon is cultivated in most hot and wet tropical regions. It grows at low altitudes and sandy soils. Its homeland is Sri Lanka. It is cultivated by its cuttings or by planting its seeds.

Religious importance and folklore:
It is believed that if cinnamon is burned in incense, it will promote high spirituality. Also used to stimulate the passions of the male, is believed to be an aphrodisiac, and studies showed that it may be helpful for impotence (Norman, 1990).
There have been many tales about cinnamon, leading to its high popularity, and here is one that traces back to the fifth century, B.C:
"It is said that huge birds bring the sticks which we call kinnamomon and put the sticks in nests, which are built of mud on steep mountains no man can climb. Yet the people living in these times employed a ruse: they cut dead asses, oxen and other such animals, into pieces as

large as possible. They then carried the meat into this place, lay it beneath the cliffs and waited hiding. The birds flew down, took the meats in their claws and back to their nests.

These meats were very heavy that the nests collapsed and fell along with the cinnamon. The people came forth and gathered the sticks which they exported to foreign countries."

Chemical structure:
Cinnamon bark contains:
- Carbohydrates
- Protein
- Fat (ether extract)
- Fiber
- Ash
- Calcium
- Phosphorus
- Iron
- Sodium
- Potassium
- Vitamins: B1, B2, C, A and Niacin (Peter, 2001).

The essential oil of the bark of this plant is rich in cinnamic aldehyde while the essential oil prepared from the leaves contains eugenol as a main constituent. The volatile oil obtained from the root, however, is rich in camphor (D'Amelio, 1999). The sweet flavor of cinnamon is due to the presence of cinnamaldehyde. The deodorizing / masking property of cinnamon bark is due to the presence of trimethyl amine.

Main use:
Cinnamon is used mainly for culinary purposes.
It is used in:
- Dessert dishes, coffee, chocolate, and as tea (bruised), mulled wines, creams and syrups;
- Beverages, boiled beef, pickles, fast food seasonings, types of cola, chutney and ketchup;
- Cakes, ice creams and other high fat desserts;
- Tobacco flavors;
- Dental and pharmaceutical preparations;
- Slowing meat spoilage;
- Anti-fungal and antibacterial capacities.

Functional properties:

This herb had been used medicinally for thousands of years to:

Fight toothache and tooth decay;

Fight urinary tract infections such as *E. coli* bacteria;

Relieve stomach irritation and help prevent ulcers;

Treat diarrhea, arthritis, bronchitis, colds, sore throat, congestion, dysentery, edema, flu, gas, hiccups, indigestion, liver problems, nausea, vomiting and several menstrual disorders;

Strengthen the heart muscle;

Assist in uterine contraction during labor and reported to be a sedative to mothers during labor (Ellen, 1997);

Relieve headaches and pain especially back pain;

Act as a detoxifying herb (Peter, 2001);

Act as an antipyretic;

Help in the burning of calories by increasing the Basic Metabolic Rate (BMR), and help in dissolving fat by its lypolytic properties;

Help in controlling body odor;

Helps diabetics control their blood sugar level, helping in the metabolism of sugar. In diabetic people, the pancreas produces insulin but the body cannot use it wisely to break down blood sugar. Cinnamon reduces the amount of insulin necessary for glucose metabolism;

Generate blood flow due to its smell, hence helping erection (Duke, 1997).

Its oil has antimicrobial activity against *Pseudomonas, Aspergillus parasiticus, Staphylococcus aureus, Candida* and *Saccharomyces cerivisiae* (Peter, 2001).

Cinnamon plays an important role in the treatment of diabetes: it contains a chemical called methoxy hydroxyl chalcone polymer, which can reduce the blood glucose level. The botanical extract of the cinnamon plant, when massaged into the scalp helps preserve the darkness of dark hair and prevents hair loss (D'Amelio, 1999). According to some people it can stimulate passion for males.

Toxicity:

Cinnamon handlers are more prone to asthma, skin irritation and hair loss. Tooth pastes and ointments containing cinnamon may cause stomatitis and dermatitis in some cases. It is not advisable to use cinnamon during pregnancy or in case of fever. The concentrated oil is more likely to cause problems such as cough and asthma, eye pain, and irritation of the skin due to the exposure to cinnamon dust.

The irritation of the skin is due to the presence of aldehyde and phenolic components, as cinnamon is made up of 78-88% of aldehyde and 5-6% of phenols, which are both very caustic to the skin. However, considering the dilution of this essential oil in a massage blend and the large area it is applied to, the risk of skin irritation is greatly reduced (Clarke, 2002).

Chapter 7

Clove: English
Karayampu : (Malayalam)
Lavang : (Hindi)

Introduction:
Scientific Name: *Syzygium aromaticum*
Family Name: *Myrtaceae*

The clove tree begins flowering after about seven years and continues to produce for another 80 years. The name is derived from the French word "clou" meaning nail, due to its appearance. The tree is of medium size, superior, evergreen, growing as tall as 20m in height. Cloves are unopened flower buds of a small evergreen tree. They are born in small clusters at the ends of branches, greenish turning pink at maturity. The seeds are soft and grooved on one side. They are also called *Eugenia caryophyllus*, *Carophyllus aromaticus* and *Flores caryophylli* (D'Amelio, 1999).

As discussed by Peter (2001), the main products of clove are:
    Whole and ground clove buds;
    Essential oils, produced from clove buds, stem and leaf ;
    Clove oleoresins.

Whole cloves should be kept in airtight containers in a dark, cool place. The major component of clove bud oil and clove stem oil is eugenol, which constitutes 70-95% of the plant constituents. The bud oil is the premium product, used as a food flavoring and seasoning blend in gradient and in high quality perfumes.

To obtain the spice, the buds must be picked when the heads develop a pink color, or just before they open. If flowers open, they have no value as a spice.

Habitat:
Clove is native to the Molucca Islands. In 1770 it was introduced into Mauritius and Reunion, and then brought to Zanzibar and Pemba.

Clove can be found in Sri Lanka, India, and Malaysia, and some African countries mainly Zanzibar and Madagascar (Shobana *et al.*, 2000). Improper storage causes loss of oil due to evaporation.

Religious importance:

It is believed that Clove worn in an amulet drives away negativity and hostility, and stops gossip. It is often carried to stimulate the memory and can be added to attraction sachets. It is placed in sachets with mint and rose to chase away melancholy and help is sound sleeping.

The oil was once used as a stimulant and local anesthetic, such as for toothaches. Long ago, Chinese people used cloves to sweeten their breath before talking to an emperor.

Natives in the Molucca Islands planted a clove tree for each newborn child. They believed that the child's fate was linked to the fate of the tree.

Main use:

Clove is used in mainly culinary purposes and as a flavoring agent due to its sweet and strong aromatic flavor. It is found in:

> Meat, such as corned beef and stews, as a pickling solution;
> Ham, to stud its fat content;
> Luncheon meat;
> Spreads and salad dressings;
> Baked beans;
> Pot roast;
> Roasted chicken or turkey;
> Curry powder;
> Mustard;
> Rice and onion-rolls;
> Chinese and Indonesian cookery;
> Breads;
> Sausages (sweet Italian);
> Tomato ketchup.

Cloves are used in sweet dishes such as fruit cakes, biscuits and mulled wine, and are very important to apple-based recipes. Care is needed when using and storing cloves because excessive heat will volatize and dissipate the aromatic essential oils, and high humidity will produce caking. Prolonged exposure to the air can cause some aroma and flavor loss, as well.

Medicinal and functional properties:

Besides being a good source of natural flavor, clove contains several basic nutrients such as proteins, water, fat, carbohydrates and ash.

In addition, it contains several minerals and vitamins, such as: Fe, Na, Ca, K, Thiamin, Riboflavin, Niacin, Ascorbic acid and vitamin A. The bud yields 15 to 18% of volatile oil containing 70% of Eugenol, 15% eugenol acetate and 12% of β -caryophyllene. The buds also contain sterols and flavonoids (D'Amelio, 1999). Clove is a high energy food.

Most of clove's properties are due to the volatile oil present in it. It has several functions, such as:

Pain relief;

Digestive aid;

Cure for stomach disorders (Peter, 2001);

Aromatic stimulant;

Antispasmodic;

Promoting sweating with fevers;

Having carminative properties;

Being an anticarcinogenic agent due to its content of Sesquiterpenes (Zheng *et al.*, 1992). (Since it can inflame the intestinal mucosa (Ellen, 1997), people with ulcers in the intestine should not eat clove).

Its antimicrobial activities: clove buds are a good source of antimicrobial agents, acting against oral bacteria that are commonly associated with dental caries and periodontal disease (Cai and Wu, 1996);

Its larvicidal and anthelmintic properties (D'Amelio, 1999);

Soothing pain caused by rheumatism;

Treating asthma and various allergic disorders if administered orally (Kim and Lee , 1998);

A potent bactericide, nematicide and fungicide (Martini *et al.*, 1996);

At certain concentrations, restricting the growth of *Listeria monocytogenes* in foods such as meat and cheese.

Hence clove oil can be considered as a natural preservative in meat and cheese (Vrinda and Garg, 2001).

It has got antioxidant activity due to the inhibition of lipo oxygenase dependent enzymatic lipid peroxidation. The inhibitory effect of cloves were found to be concentration dependent. 0.5 mg of cloves brings about 100% inhibition of antioxidant activity. Of all spices, clove showed the highest antioxidant activity (Shobana *et al.*, 2000). Clove extracts exhibited the antioxidant activities by inhibiting the malonaldehyde (MA) formation in blood plasma (Lee and Shiba-moto, 2001).

The strong antioxidant activities of Cloves are due to the presence of eugenol, and more specifically the phenolic components present in the eugenol (Lee and Takayuki, 2001).

The presence of aroma chemicals in cloves is the reason it improves food stability. The ingestion of these compounds helps prevent:
1. *In vivo* oxidation damage;
2. Lipid peroxidation, associated with many diseases such as cancer;
3. Arteriosclerosis, diabetes and immune deficiency (Lee and Takayuki, 2001).

Toxicity:

Clove buds should be avoided by people with extremely sensitive skin or having a history and dermatitis, as it might cause irritation, due to the presence of aldehyde and phenolic components which are found in large amounts in essential oil of cloves. However, considering the dilution of this essential oil in a massage blend and the large area it is applied to, the risk of skin irritation is greatly reduced.

Many experiments have studied for the Lethal Dose$_{50}$ (LD$_{50}$) of the clove, with the following results:
1. For the buds, the LD$_{50}$ is 2.65 g/kg body weight
2. For the stems, the LD$_{50}$ is 2.03 g/kg body weight.
3. For the leaves, the LD$_{50}$ is equal to 1.37 g/kg body weight (Clarke, 2002).

The amounts entering the body in aroma therapy using inhalation are negligible; it is therefore safe.

Chapter 8

Cumin: English
Jirakam : (*Malayalam*)
Jira : (*Hindi*)

Introduction:
Scientific Name: *Cuminum cyminum*
Family Name*: Umbelliferae*
Cumin is considered to be a strong aromatic seed of dried ripe fruits of *Cuminum cyminum L.* Widely known as: cumin, kummel, zireh-e sabz, cumino, kemon, zira, kamun (Peter, 2001).

Cumin is an annual plant derived from the *Umbelliferae* family, and is native to Egypt. It is also found in Iran, India, Mexico, China, Saudi Arabia, and now in Sicily and Malta. It is considered one of the most important spices in the world, and is used as a constituent in many food industries. Cumin seed oil is obtained by steam distillation and is used in the manufacturing of perfumes and fragrances. It is mainly used as a cookery spice.

Cumin stem is slim and branched, approximately one foot high and angular. The leaves are divided into long, narrow segments like fennel, but are smaller, and have a deep green color. The upper leaves are nearly stalkless, but the lower ones have longer leaf-stalks. The flowers are small, rose or white -colored and bloom in June and July, being succeeded by fruit - the so-called seeds - which constitute the Cumin of pharmacy. They are oblong in shape, thicker in the middle, and almost straight. The odor and taste are similar to that of caraway, but less agreeable (Grieve, 1972). Cumin is considered a cold-season crop on the plains and as a summer-season crop in the hills. Black Cumin seeds (*Cuminum nigrum*), known as Kashmiri cumin, which tastes like caraway seed, and is used by Moguls, grow in Kashmir and Iran, and is more costly.

Chemical structure:
Cumin has about 2-4.5% of volatile oil and 10% of fixed oil. Its odor

and flavor is due primarily to the presence of aldehyde, such as cuminic aldehyde, or cuminol. The composition of cumin seed oil was a topic of interest for many years. "In 1981, it was reported that cumin oil contained mint sulfide as a trace element" (Takahashi, 1981). Twelve years later, the main constituents of Egyptian cumin seed oil were found to be: cumin aldehyde, β-pinene, γ - terpinene and ρ-cymene .

The composition of the Turkish cumin seed oil was investigated later on and characterized by a high amount of cumin aldehyde and perilla aldehyde.

History and folklore:

As it is told by Mrs. Grieve: "Cumin is mentioned in Isaiah xxvii. 25 and 27, and Matthew xxii. 23, and in the works of Hippocrates and Dioscorides. From Pliny we learn that the ancients took the ground seed medicinally with bread, water or wine, and that it was accounted the best of condiments. The seeds of the Cumin when smoked, were found to occasion pallor of the face, whence the expression of Horace, *exsangue cuminum*, and Pliny tells us that the followers of the celebrated rhetorician Porcius Latro employed it to produce a complexion such as bespeaks application to study."

Cumin also symbolized greediness among the Greeks; Marcus Aurelius was so nicknamed because of his avariciousness, and misers were jocularly said to have eaten Cumin. Germans bake bread with cumin as they believed that the spice prevented stealing by wood demons. Also, girls baked bread with cumin seeds to keep their lovers faithful (Ellen, 1997).

Cumin has now gone out of use in European medicine. And even though it got replaced by caraway seed, which has a more agreeable flavor, it is still used in large amounts in Indian cuisine (Grieve, 1972).

Main use:

Cumin is used because of its strong aromatic smell and warm, bitterish taste. It is mainly used for :
Condiments and flavoring in eastern dishes and bread;
Marinades for chicken, turkey, lamb and pork;
Olive oil when stir-frying vegetables;
Confectionery.

Cumin is used in food processing as a preservative, and in the preparation of certain dishes during periods of fasting to make up for the lack of meat, taking the place of proteins found in our everyday diet.

The flavor of cumin is considered a major constituent in Mexican, Thai, Vietnamese and Indian cuisines. Cumin is an essential ingredient of chili powder, and is found in achiote blends, adobos, garam masala, curry powder and baharat.

Medicinal and functional properties:

Cumin is used for several purposes such as:
> A stimulant agent;
> An antispasmodic agent;
> A carminative agent;
> An antimicrobial agent;
> The treatment flatulence, diarrhea and digestive disorders;
> The treatment of wounds (Peter, 2001);
> Preventing cellulite problem by massaging with the oil;
> An ingredient in perfumes (Ellen,1997);
> Diuretic, anthelmintic, uterine and nervine stimulent.
> Also used for haemorrhoids, leucorrhea, skin diseases,
> leprosy, leucoderma, fever, ophthalmopathy, gonorrhea,
> asthama and bronchitis (Warrier *et al.*, 1994).

Cumin seeds, a commonly consumed spice, have been found to be very beneficial for diabetes patients as it has anti-diabetic effects. An eight-week dietary regimen containing 1.25% of cumin powder was found to have enormous results, in the reduction in hyperglycemia and glucosuria. This was accompanied by improvement in the body weights of diabetics who followed a cumin diet. Dietary cumin causes other metabolic alterations, as well, which include: lowered blood urea level and reduced excretion of urea and creatinine by diabetics (Willatgamuwa *et al.*, 1998). Cumin has an impact against the bacteria that causes body odor, so it can be used as a deodorant herb in its powder form and be rubbed on to the underarm.

In addition, cumin has three pain relieving compounds, seven anti-inflammatory and four that combat swelling (Duke, 1997).

Toxicity:

Allergy to the aromatic spice cumin has been diagnosed a few times, but rarely. Symptoms are nausea, shortness of breath, itching and vomiting (Boxer *et al.*, 1997).

Chapter 9

Curry Leaf: English
Kari Veppila: (Malayalam)
Curry patta: (Hindi)

Introduction:
Scientific Name: *Murraya koenigii*
Family Name: *Rutaceae*

Curry leaf is a perennial leaf vegetable. It is mainly cultivated in mountainous regions and grows up to an elevation of 1500 m.

In South India, curry leaves are cultivated in every house for use in the food preparation, as fresh leaves, to get the aroma.

The leaves of the plant are employed extensively as flavoring in curries like "Dal," "South Indian Sambar" and many South Indian dishes, such as fish curry, vegetables and meat preparations. If kept in airtight containers it can be stored for a long time, and leaves retain their flavor even after drying.

Chemical structure:
Curry leaves contain the following free amino acids: asparagine, serine, aspartic acid, glutamic acid, threonine, alanine, proline, tyrosine, tryptophan, leucine and lysine.
The fruit is edible.
It yields 0.76% of a yellow volatile oil with neroli-like odor and a pepper-like taste accompanied by an agreeable, cool sensation on the tongue. It can be considered a cold food.

The oil constituents are:
> Palmitic acid;
> Lauric acid;
> Cadinol;
> Cadinene;
> Isosafrol;

Caryophyllene;
d-sabiene.

Based on several analyses, it was found that curry leaves contain the following nutrients:

Moisture;
Protein;
Fat;
Carbohydrate;
Fiber;
Mineral matter;
Calcium;
Phosphorus;
Iron;
Carotene;
Nicotinic acid;
Vitamin C;
Thiamine and riboflavin.

Extraction of the bark of *M. koenigii* with petroleum ether gave the following carbazole alkaloids:

1) Girinimbine (Chakraborty *et al.*,1964);
2) Murrrayanine (1-methoxy-3formylcarbazole-Chakraborty *et al.*, 1965);
3) Optically inactive mahanimbine (Roy and Chakraborty, 1974).

Other isolated alkaloids and produced are:

1) Murraycine (Chakraborty and Das, 1968; Chakraborty *et al.*,1971);
2) Mukanol (Bhattacharya and Chakraborty, 1984); and
3) Murrayazolidine (Chakraborty *et al.*,1970).

The stem of *M. koenigii* on alcholic extract produced mukoeic acid (1-methoxycarbazole-3carboxylic acid (Chowdhury and Chakraborty, 1971). The Fruits of *M. koenigii* produced a new alkaloid namely koenimbine (Narasinmhan *et al.*, 1968).The leaves of *M. koenigii* produced a number of alkaloids, namely koenigicine, koenimbine, (Kureel *et al.*, 1969), cyclomahanimbine, bicyclomahanimbine and mahanimbine. In addition, other constituents yelded from the leaves are coumarinic glucoside, scopolin and carbazole alkaloid murrayanine (Gupta and Nigam, 1970).

The petrolium extract of the root of *M. koenigii* yielded a carbozole alkaloid, mahanimboline (Roy *et al.*, 1979).

The root on extraction with hexane also yielded girinimbine (Joshi *et al.*,1970), and with benzene extract gave two new carbazole alkaloids: muloline and mukolindine with structures 6-hydroxymethyl-1-methoxy-carbazole and 6-formyl-1-methoxy carbazole respectively (Roy *et al.*,1982).

The steam distillation under pressure of fresh leaves of *M. koenigii* produced the following essential oils:
1) Dl-α-phellandrene;
2) D-sabinene;
3) D-α-pinene;
4) D-αterpinol;
5) Isosafrol;
6) Caryophyllene;
7) Cadinene;
8) Cadvirol;
9) Lauric acid and palmitic acid (Dutt, 1958).

However, the oil yielded by water distillation of the leaves produced only: 1-α-pinene, 1-sabinine, dipentene, 1-terpinol, 1-caryophyllene and 1-cadinine (Nigam and Purohit, 1961).

Medicinal and functional use:

Curry leaf is used in traditional medicine. It has been reported that it has tonic, stomachic and carminative properties.

The essential oil of *M. koenigii* showed antibacterial effects against *B. subtillis, S. aureus, C. pyogenes, Proteus vulgaris* and *Pasturella multocida*. The essential oil from leaves of *M. koenigii* showed antifungal effects against *Cadida albicans, C. tropicalis, Aspergllus niger, A. fumigatus* and *Microsporum gypseum* (Goutam and Purohit, 1974).

Kishore *et al.*, (1982) showed fungi toxicity against *Colletotrichum falcatum* and *Rhizoctonia solani* with the ethanolic extract of the leaves. The ethanolic extracts of the whole plant of *M. koenigii* produced antiprotozoal action against *Entamoeba histolytica*. It also has an antispasmodic effect on isolated guinea pig ileum (Bhakuni *et al.*, 1969, Satyavati *et al.*, 1987). It has an important role in the treatment of diabetes and in antioxidant activity (Peter, 2001).

Roots and bark paste are applied externally for skin eruption and poisonous bites. Green leaves are used in dysentery and as febrifuge in India (Satyavati *et al.*, 1987).

The plants can also be used for helminthiasis, leucoderma, colic, flatulence and leprosy (Warrier *et al.*, 1995).

Chapter 10

Dill : **English**
Sathakuppa : (*Malayalam*)
Soya: (*Hindi*)

Introduction:
Scientific Name: *Anethum graveolens*
Family Name: *Apiaceae(Umbelleferae)*

The spice Dill got its name from its effect of lulling babies, by mixing it in grape water for the treatment of colic, because "Dilla" means "lull" (Ellen, 1997).

Dill has feather-like light green leaves and a hollow stem. It is a member of the parsley family, and a delicately flavored and aromatic herb. The ancient Egyptians have been said to have used dill for medicinal purposes. It is an annual aromatic, branched herb. Its leaves have been used in flavoring of soups, sausages, curries, gravies, salads and much more (Elisabeth, 1992). In some countries the leaves are steamed with rice, whereas fruits are used in flavoring native confectionery. The herb oil has a powerful sweet spicy, peppery, and aromatic odor, evocative of spearmint oil with a sweet nutmeg-like feeling. The taste is warm and slightly burning, but pleasant (Peter, 2001).

Habitat:
The climate, and well-drained soil of North America are perfect for the proper growth of this annual 2 - 3 feet tall herb. Dill is characterized by long, dissected leaves and compound, radiating umbels, and it resembles a small fennel plant. Dill is native to Mediterranean countries and southern Russia, and has roots in southern Europe and western Asia, also. It is cultivated in India and North and South America as well.

Religious importance and folklore:

It is believed that burned dried seeds of this herb protect a home.
When added to baths (just one drop), dill will increase a person's attractiveness and enhance physical "chemistry" leading to greater love.

The ancient Greeks thought of dill as a sign of wealth.
Hippocrates himself wrote of a recipe for cleaning the mouth in which you rinse it with dill seed that has been boiled in white wine. During the Middle Ages, dill was considered to have extraordinary powers and was used against witchcraft. If someone thought a witch had cast a spell on him, he would make himself special drinks containing dill leaves to be protected from the spell. Charlemagne used to offer his guests Dill, if at his table and being attacked with hiccups.

Chemical structure:

It was found that dill oil contains limonene, carvone, myrcene, α-pinene and α-phellandrene. The main compounds of the herb oil are phellandrene and limonene, whereas ketone increases from 12% (vegetative stage) to 22% (maximum bloom) and rises to 35% at the milky-wax stage. The aroma of the dill herb is due to the concentration of five components namely dill-furan, α-phellandrene, limonene, myrsticin and p-mentha dienbutyrate (Peter, 2001).

Main use:

The leaves and the dried fruit (seeds) of the dill plant are both used. Dill cannot be subjected to long cooking times because it looses its delicate flavor when dried, although it does freeze well. It is an herb that does better on its own. It is used splendidly in salmon dishes, in thick soups that are cream based, in many dishes calling for sour cream or yogurt, in egg dishes, sauces, seafood, and vegetables. Some sour cream added to dill leaves will complete a bowl of Potato Cheese Soup. Dill is often used as a condiment in European cooking; it is combined with pickled vegetables such as cucumbers and is used in fish sauces and soups.

It is also excellent in wine vinegar. Fresh leaves in plastic should be stored in the refrigerator. Dried dill and dill seeds are to be stored in airtight containers on a pantry shelf.

Medicinal and functional properties:

Dill leaves are nutritious elements; they contain lots of minerals, such as calcium, phosphorus and iron, as well as nine amino acids and flavanoids.

The oil has:

> Antibacterial properties;
> An important role in the protection of food from contamination during storage (Foster, 1999).

> On the other hand, dill fruit has:
> Carminative effects;
> Aromatic stimulant properties;
> Stomachic and diuretic properties;
> Relieves flatulence, colic pain and vomiting. Treats gastric disorders in children according to Ellen (1997).

The fruits of Dill are also used for cough, asthma, bronchitis, ulcers, syphilis, hemorrhoids, fever, ulcers, intestinal worms and cardiac debility (Warrier *et al.*, 1994).

Chapter 11

Garlic: English
Veluthulli, Vellulli: (Malayalam)
Lasun : (Hindi)

Introduction:
Scientific Name: *Allium sativum*
Family Name: *Liliaceae*

Garlic is one of the traditional medicinal herbs, found in several countries, such as Egypt, Sumeria, China and Europe. Historically, it was used in China due to its blood pressure-lowering effects, in Egypt for increasing in the physical strength, and finally in Europe to prevent Plague (Mar and Bent, 1999). It is considered the second most widely cultivated Allium after onion.

Nowadays, garlic is used for its flavor, aroma and taste, being prepared domestically and by a variety of food manufacturing processes, resulting in a variety of forms, such as powder or paste (Brodnitz *et al.*, 1971). Dehydrated garlic in powder or granulated form has replaced fresh garlic in industrial uses (Fenwick and Hanley, 1986 a and b).

Habitat:
The frost-hardy, bulbous perennial herb needs moderate soil, ample sunlight and warmth. The plant grows to two feet tall.

Religious importance:
It is believed that peeled garlic cloves placed in a room wards off diseases, and if hung in a new home, dispels negativity and evil.

Chemical structure:
Garlic contains sulfur-rich derivatives of the amino acid cysteine-alline. When the fresh tissue of the raw garlic is damaged, the flavor precursor reacts under the control of the enzyme alliinase S-alk (en)yl-

L-cysteine sulphoxide Lyase to release the highly reactive sulphenic acids plus ammonia and pyruvate (Block, 1985).The enzyme alliinase is confined to the cell vacuole whereas flavor precursors are restrained to the cytoplasm probably within small vesicles associated with their presence in the cell. Allicin breaks down after 20 minutes of cooking or after a few hours at natural room temperature (Gebhardt, 1993).

Main use:
Garlic is used all around the world for its flavoring properties.
It can be used as a fresh product on main salads, as a dressing along with oil or lime, in pizzas, and finally, in all kinds of stew. Processed, is used in: mayonnaise, salad dressings, tomato products, soups and several meat products.
Raw garlic, is used in the preparation of garlic powder, garlic salt, garlic vinegar, garlic pickles, garlic cheese croutons, and potato chips.

Medicinal and functional properties:
Garlic has been considered a good source of carbohydrates, proteins and phosphorus. Green garlic has been recently reported to contain Ascarobic acid, as well. It has several properties, such as: excellent carminative, stimulation of cell growth and activity, nerve tonic, antiseptic agent and cholesterol lowering effects, due to the presence of allicin (Warshafsky *et al.*, 1993), lowering blood pressure, platelet aggregation. Garlic is an important factor in treating cardiovascular disease. It inhibits platelets activation (Bordia, 1978).

It has an effect on blood coagulation and fibrinolytic activity which are factors in the development of thrombosis (De Boer and Folts, 1989). It reduces the risk of stomach cancer; various constituents have been found to inhibit tumor growth, notably due to garlic-derived organosulphides. It has antioxidant properties.

The following actions of garlic was reported:
Antibiotic effects, such as the treatment of wounds, was reported by Adetumbi and Lau (1983);
Antifungal properties (Caporaso *et al.*, 1983);
Antimicrobial properties (Hughes and Lawson, 1991);
Garlic is also used to treat flatulence, colic, constipation,

hemorrhoids, leprosy, pulmonary and laryngeal tuberculosis, leucoderma, hysteria, sciatica, lumbago, asthma, facial paralysis and dental caries (Warrier *et al.*, 1994).

More properties:
a) Garlic and the heart:
A number of studies have shown that garlic consumption decreases total and LDL cholesterol as well as triglyceride level.

For instance, a consumption of 0.5-1 g of garlic per day lowers the cholesterol level by 10% (Warshafsky *et al.*, 1994). This decrease is due to the effect of garlic in decreasing cholesterol and fatty acid synthesis as well as cholesterol absorption (Chi *et al.*, 1982).

However, some active components may be lost during processing or released upon the crushing of garlic, during the drying process, from the temperature at which it is dried, and finally, due to humidity (Chutani and Bordia, 1981).

Garlic has also been found to draw out antithrombotic effects and slightly decrease blood pressure (5.5mm Hg) decrease in systolic blood pressure and small decrease in diastolic) Its antioxidant property is due to the fact that aged garlic contains allyl amino acid derivatives, stable lipid-soluble allyl sulfides, flavonoids and saponins. The water soluble organosulfur compounds, S-allylcysteine and S-allyl mercaptocyteine, have potent anti-oxidant properties (Lawson, 1993). In addition, aged garlic extract contains lipid-soluble compounds such as diallyl sulfide, triallyl sulfide, diallyl disulfide and diallyl polysulfide, that have antioxidant properties as well (Ernst, 1985).

b) Garlic and blood sugar:
Many studies have proven that garlic has the property of reducing blood sugar levels by promoting the pathway that takes up sugar in the blood and transforms it into carbohydrate stored in the liver (Fulder, 1997).

Another effect is that garlic increases insulin secretion, which inhibit the build up of excess sugars in the blood (Chang and Johnson, 1980). This does not make garlic a "cure" or a treatment for diabetes, however, it will help in cases of pre-diabetes or poor sugar metabolism (Jain *et al.*, 1973).

c) **Garlic and cancer:**

Garlic is considered a potent inhibitor of tumorigenesis (Belman,1983). Diallyl sulfide and diallyl disulfide appear to be the bioactive components of garlic that exert the anticarcinogenic effect (Wagovich, 1987).

These allylic compounds arouse glutathione S-transferase activity in the liver, which binds to and detoxifies potential carcinogens.
"Organosulfur components found in garlic appear to have antioxidant with free-radical-scavenging properties to inhibit lipid peroxidation."
Garlic may also well suppress the tumor promotion phase of carcinogens by reducing polyamine formation, by the simple fact that they inhibit ornithine decarboxylase and stimulate DNA repair (Weisberger and Pensky, 1957).

d) **Garlic and toxicity:**

Since the using up of sulfur containing ingredients of garlic that are supposed to be toxic is low, acute fatal garlic poisoning in humans is very rare. If taken in extremely large amounts, it may cause:

> Anemia, stomach ulcers, severe allergic reaction, suppression of testicular functions, gastrointestinal discomfort, bloating, headaches, sweating, light-headedness, menorrhagia and bad odor (Schulz *et al.*, 1997).

It might also produce contact dermatitis, asthma, and anaphylaxis (Jappe *et al.*, 1999).
It has been associated with postoperative bleeding and a spontaneous spinal hematoma in an 87-year old man (Burnham, 1995).
 The best dose to be taken is 0.6-1.2 grams of dried powder or 2-4 grams of fresh garlic daily.

Eating garlic with fatty meals:

Many studies have been performed on the consumption of garlic at the same time as fatty meals, and the results showed that consuming garlic with 100 g of butter, (butter is considered an animal fat which is made of saturated fatty acids and leads to heart problems such as strokes, heart failure, and clot-formation) resulted a ten percent increase in blood cholesterol for a few hours, accompanied by a twenty percent decrease in anti-clot formation in the blood (Sainani *et al.*, 1979).

From this we understand that eating garlic with fatty meals helps the accumulation of adipose tissues (body fat) more easily. Garlic helps in the prevention of many health problems, and for this reason it is important to use in meals, however it is ineffective in undoing or reversing certain already-existing health problems (Bordia *et al.*, 1975).

How to deal with the odor of garlic:

Everyone knows that when it comes to eating garlic, it is helpful to have chewing gum or anything else that might remove or hide the bad breath that will appear. Garlic's strong odor comes mainly from the sulfides and disulfides present in it. When garlic is eaten, the bad smell comes mainly from your mouth and teeth, but some will come from the stomach, lungs and skin, as well. This bad "aroma" appears when garlic is crushed, causing the sulfides to be released.

The best way to eat garlic is ingesting it already-crushed, washing it down with a liquid, or eating it without chewing, by making it into a "pill" with other food items such as lettuce or parsley (Fulder, 1997).

Chapter 12

Ginger: English
Ingi :(Malayalam)
Adarak: (Hindi)

Introduction:

Scientific Name: *Zingiber officinale*
Family Name: *Zingiberaceae*

Ginger is a herbaceous tropical perennial. The entire plant is lusciously aromatic, but its underground rhizome is considered the spice. This rhizome can either be used fresh or dried. It can reach up to 12 cm in length and 3.5 cm in height. It has a starchy, resinous and fibrous texture (Peter, 2001).

All the surfaces of ginger are striated longitudinally and have a few thread-like projecting strands of conducting tissue. The taste is pungent and aromatic (D'Amelio, 1999).

Ginger is cultivated in several regions of the world, such as: India, China, Nigeria, Sierra Leone, Indonesia, Bangladesh, and Australia. It is scattered in huge quantities all across the North America, with a height of 6 inches (Peter, 2001).

Religious importance:
It is believed that ginger is used in passion spells to "heat up" relationships and to ensure the success of spells in general.

Ginger and folklore:
Ginger has been well-known for years; with the gingerbread boy story being passed down from parents to children through the ages. The main character-loved by everyone- had the name of every ones favorite spice. The tale is an allegory for ginger circulating in the

body: moving quickly, overcoming obstacles, and warming up the system, just like the main character. Ginger was also found in the "Hansel and Gretel" folktale, where the house of the evil witch was covered in gingerbread. In this tale the spicy aroma of the ginger was considered a homey spice which would attract people.

Chemical structure:

The ginger rhizome contains steam volatile oils such as Zingiberene and Curcumene, fixed fatty oil, pungent compounds, oleoresin such as Gingerol and Shogaols (D'Amelio, 1999), proteins, cellulose, pentosans, starch and mineral elements. The two most important factors present in ginger are the protease and the antioxidants.

Main use:

The refreshing, pleasant aroma, sharp taste and carminative property of ginger make it a crucial ingredient in food processing. Fresh ginger is unique for its flowery flavor and spicy taste. It is usually diluted in olive oil by a percentage of 20-25% of essential oil (D'Amelio, 1999). In African countries, the fragrant flowers are the source of fragrance. Ginger is used as a preservative in the manufacturing of chocolate. It is also used as well in the production of alcoholic beverages. Fruits are used in washing clothes to fix the colors (Duke, 1985).For Europeans, Ginger is considered as a dessert nut. For the Chinese, Ginger is an essential constituent; they use it in most of their meals, such as chicken with Ginger and Mushrooms, and Shrimps and Ginger.

Medicinal and functional properties:

Ginger is excellent at:
Inhibiting hypercholesterolemia (Gujral *et al.*, 1978);
Inhibiting cataracts (Duke, 1997);
Inhibiting arthritic pain (D'Amelio, 1999);
Treating bascillary dysentery as an antiseptic (D'Amelio, 1999);
Treating body odor;
Treating menstrual cramps, infertility, inhibited sexual desire in women, and erection problems in men;
Treating amenorrhea;
Treating ulcers, tendonitis and seborrhea;

Treating angina, a form of heart disease that causes chest pain.
Angina is caused by atherosclerosis (Duke, 1997), when
cholesterol deposits lead to a narrowing of the arteries;
Controlling obesity;
Strengthening and healing the respiratory system;
Fighting off colds and flu;
Reducing inflammaton (D'Amelio, 1999);
Soothing sore throats and relieving headaches and body aches
(Mustafa and Srivastava, 1990).

Ginger contains more than twelve antioxidants which help neutralize
the free radicals which cause inflammation (Duke, 1997) and removes
congestion. Ginger is recommended during pregnancy for treating
morning sickness, vomiting, nausea (Bone *et al.*, 1990), motion
sickness (Mowrey and Claysion, 1982), digestive problems and for
colds and sore throats. The oil found in the ginger plant is used as a
stimulant and given to those with poor memory, as well (D'Amelio,
1999).

In addition, it has been found that:
Ginger is an excellent antioxidant, which may be linked to the
prevention of certain cancers, coronary heart disease, and in
preserving lipid-based foods (Shoji *et al.*, 1982);
Due to its linalool content, it can act as an anticonvulsive and
antiseptic;
It inhibits prostaglandins, stimulates bile secretion and assists
the liver (Rattan, 1988);
It is an excellent muscle relaxant;
It has an analgesic effect;
It extends meat's shelf life;
It has antimicrobial activity, in relation to *Bacillus subtillis, E. coli*
and *Mycobacterium* (Peter, 2001);
It has an influence on the eicosanoids cascade, with influence
Functions such as wound healing, inflammation reduction and
platelets aggregation; and also reduces in arteriosclerosis Rattan,
1988). It has many additional health benefits, as well, such as
enhancing gastrointestinal motility, and treating of stomach
aches, vomiting and indigestion (Al-Yahya *et al.*, 989). It is an
excellent stimulant for the hair follicles (D'Amelio, 1999). A
recent study is investigating the anti tumor properties of
Gingerol, especially in inhibiting skin cancer (Fulder, 1996).

Ginger can also be used as an anthelmintic and carminative, used to treat asthma, diarrhea, flatulence, cholera and elephantiasis (Warrier *et al.* 1996).

Ginger and diet:

Firstly ginger's most important role in the diet is that its components act as stevedores, carrying food across the stomach and into circulation (Fulder, 1996).

Secondly, the proteases present in considerable amounts are catalytic substances that act as natural meat tenderizers. Ginger also has a substance similar to protease: the lipase, which helps in the digestion of fat (Connell, 1970).

Finally, the antioxidants found in ginger not only prevent food rancidity and spoilage but also prevent oxidation to occur in our bodies. Oxidation leads to the formation of free radicals, which may lead to many degenerative diseases such as arteriosclerosis. Ginger, by preventing oxidation in our bodies, will not only reduce the occurrence of these diseases, but will prevent the rise of cholesterol levels in our blood, and with no oxidation, the cholesterol can be easily lowered. (Mahan, 2003).

Ginger and blood clotting:

Blood clotting occurs when cell fragments called platelets stick to the plaque on the inside of narrowed arteries, forming a small slump. These clots may lead to heart attacks and strokes (cerebrovascular accidents) (Rattan, 1988). Micro clots can occur as well, restricting circulation. Ginger was found to make the blood less sticky, by producing lesser amounts of thromboxane and prostaglandins, which are local chemical messengers leading to blood and heart disease. Ginger was shown to have a similar effect as aspirin on blood clotting (Atal *et al.*, 1981).

Ginger and toxicity:

Many researches have confirmed the safety of ginger utilization. Nevertheless, we should be careful because even the safest food, if taken in a wrong way (in excess for instance), can cause unfavorable effects. For example, ginger is not recommended for people with a high fever. In addition, in cases when some one has a rapid pulse, red skin, red tongue, dehydration and blood in the stools, ginger is not recommended, since it can make these symptoms worse (Fulder, 1996).

Chapter 13

*Kokam and Cambodge:*English
Kotappuli: (Malayalam)
Bilatti amli: (Hindi)

Introduction:

Scientific Name: *Garcinia indica, Garcinia cambogia*
HCA (hydroxycitric acid).
Family Name: *Guttiferae: Clusiaceae*

Garcinia is the genus name of a group of herbs in the family *Guttiferae,* including more than 200 species of slow-growing trees and shrubs found in Asia, Polynesia and South Africa (Foster, 1999).

Kokam is a small, slim, evergreen tree with drooping branches, which taking on a pyramidal shape upon maturity. It prefers shade and is associated with fire-protected secondary forests. The juice of its fruits is used as mordant. The kokam fruit has an agreeable flavor and Swedish acid taste. The normal shelf-life of the fruit is five days (Peter, 2001).

Cambodge is a tropical fruit called Malabar tamarind. It is a small or medium-sized evergreen tree found mostly in India.
It has a rounded crown and shiny dark green leaves up to five inches long and three inches wide (Anon, 1956). The fruits may vary in weight, 50-180 g. Cambodge fruit has an excellent therapeutic value and the dried rind is a popular fruit spice used in cookery.

Historical perspective:
Garcinia cambogia is a yellowish, pumpkin-shaped tropical fruit native to the country of India. In 1965, researches identified HCA as the principle acid found in the fruit and rind of *Garcinia cambogia.* (Lewis and Neelakantan, 1965).

In 1970, researcher studied the action of HCA on fatty acid synthesis, leading to the discovery that *Garcinia cambogia* can inhibit lipogenesis and treat lipid disorders as well as obesity. However it cannot affect energy production by the body (Sullivan *et al.*, 1972).

Around 1990, the plant was found to be a competitive inhibitor of ATP citrate Lyase, an enzyme that is involved in the conversion of carbohydrate to fat (Sullivan *et al.*, 1977).

Chemical structure:

Kokam contains malic acid, tartaric and citric acid. It also contains moisture, protein, crude fiber, total ash, tannins, pectin, starch, crude fat, ascorbic acid and carbohydrates. Kokam butter is rich in stearic and oleic acids (Peter, 2001).

However, cambodge contains citric acid in a higher proportion, 10.6% of tartaric acid, 15% of reducing sugars and 1.52% of phosphoric acid. New chemical constituents were isolated from the *Garcinia gambogia* plant. One Xanthone was isolated from the root: garbogiol (rheediaxanthone A) and two benzophenones from the bark: garcinol and isogarcinol (Iinuma *et al.*, 1998). Other very important constituents of *Garcinia cambogia* are the flavonoids (Asha *et al.*, 2001).

Main use:

The kokam rind has a very high concentration of the natural red pigment anthocyanin, and hence is used as a natural colorant for acid foods. "It is edible, nutritive, demulcent, astringent and emollient." It is also used in the preparation of red cooling syrups (Peter, 2001).

The Cambodge fruits are characterized by a sharp, but pleasant acidity. It is included in curries as an appetizer in East India. The dried rind of cambodge has antiseptic properties. It is also used as a substitute for acetic and formic acid in many applications.

Cambodge is used as a pigment in the manufacture of lacquer and in medicine. According to Indian folk tradition, *Garcinia cambogia* has been prescribed for such ailments as rheumatism and bowel complaints. Both *Garcinia cambogia* and extracted HCA are widely available in North America as components in many commercial dietary supplements.

Medicinal and functional properties:

Garcinia cambogia is listed in indigenous medicine as having high therapeutic value and is nowadays used in remedies for various diseases. Both garcinia fruits contain (-) hydroxycitric acid which is chemically similar to the citric acid found in oranges. The fruit extract of *Garcinia cambogia* was shown to be a competitive inhibitor of adenosine 5'-triphosphate (ATP) citrate Lyase (Lewis and Neelakantan, 1965), the enzyme that catalyses the extramitochondrial cleavage of citrate to oxaloacetate and acetyl CoA. (Watson and Lowenstein, 1970). This action reduces the acetyl CoA concentration, (Lowenstein, 1971) limiting the availability of two-carbon units required for the biosynthesis of fatty acids and cholesterol therefore the storage of body fat becomes impossible (Sullivan *et al.*, 1974). In addition, it increases the rate of hepatic glycogen synthesis and inhibits body weight gain (Sullivan *et al.*, 1977).

The HCA it contains is responsible for:

Hunger suppression in humans;

Inhibiting the conversion of excess CHO into fat;

Increasing stores of body's energy fuel.

Garcinia fruits lower total serum cholesterol, triglyceride and non-essential fatty acids level, these functions are due to the hydrocytric acid that is present in it by a percentage of 60%, inhibiting lipogenesis of ATP citrate-Lyase (Lewis and Neelakantan, 1965) by triggering fatty acid oxidation in the liver *via* thermogenesis. It burns the fat slowly without stimulating the nervous system. In addition, it promotes the growth of lean muscle and is safe for diabetis. In addition, although garcinia cambogia has no effect on blood glucose level, it has a lowering effect on the blood insulin level, leading to the conclusion that it improves efficient glucose metabolism (Alberti and Zimmet, 1998).

Several studies showed that after the administration of flavonoids from the *Garcinia cambogia* plant, activities of glucose-6-phosphate dehydrogenase and isocitrate dehydrogenase were significantly reduced, paired with a stimulated activity of the lipoprotein lipase and plasma lecithin cholesterol acyl transferase. Hepatic and fecal bile acids and fecal neutral sterols were elevated, leading to a higher rate in cholesterol degradation (Asha *et al.*, 2001). Flavonoids can inhibit the various stages thought to be involved in the development and formation of atherosclerosis, endothelial damage, leukocyte activation, platelet adhesion, adhesion and secretion (Beratz and Cazenave, 1988). Oxidative modification of LDL is the major key in the pathogenesis of atherosclerosis. Dietary flavonoids present in *Garcinia cambogia* (Asha *et al.*, 2001) were found to lower LDL levels and inhibit the oxidative modification of LDL (Catapano, 1997), which leads to a reduction in LDL oxidation and atherogenesis (Leonteva *et al.*, 1979). The kokam fruit is used for bilious infections, and also for the treatment of hepatitis, laryngitis, and mouth infections.

The seed's oil is used in the preparation of ointments, and suppositories, and for other pharmaceutical purposes. It has also been used for fighting ulcerations, and fissures in the lips and hands.
Oil from seeds has been used as a remedy against:

> Phthisis-pulmonalis;
> Scrofulous diseases;
> Dysentery;
> Mucous diarrhea;
> Wounds and sores;
> And also used as a substitute for spermaceti.

Garcinia cambogia does not act on the nervous system to enhance calorie -burning; it just alters the lipid and carbohydrate metabolism (Maheed *et al.*, 1994).

Toxicity and side effects:

Few adverse reactions from the use of *Garcinia cambogia* have been reported. The most common ones were headaches, and upper respiratory or gastrointestinal symptoms. However, patients taking oral hypoglycemic agents are cautioned against the use of *Garcinia cambogia*, due to the possibility of exacerbating their Hypoglycemic condition. In addition, individuals diagnosed with diabetes mellitus should use extreme caution when taking *Garcinia cambogia*, due to its glycemic action. Individuals with Alzheimer's disease and other dementia syndromes should avoid using it due to the possibility of acetyl choline formation in the brain (Peter, 2001). Finally, pregnant and lactating mothers must avoid its usage.

Chapter 14

Nutmeg and Mace : English
Jathica and Jatipatri: (Malayalam)
Jayphal and Javitri: (Hindi)
Introduction:
Scientific Name: *Myristica fragrans*
Family Name: *Myristicaceae*

Two spices are obtained from the fruit of the evergreen nutmeg tree: nutmeg and mace. When fruits are harvested, they are split open to reveal a red, lacy layer on the shell. This layer is removed and dried to become mace, and in turn the shell is dried until it cracks and becomes brown, at which point it is nutmeg (Foster, 1999). Nutmeg is one of the newer spices used for culinary purposes, first being used in cooking during about 12th century. Nutmeg and mace are two different parts of the same nutmeg tree. The major nutmeg-growing areas are Indonesia and Grenada. Nutmeg originating from East India has a relatively high volatile oil content and a distinctively rich flavor and aroma.

Nutmeg is a conical tree reaching a height of 4-10 meters. The fruits are pendulous, broadly pyriform, yellow, soft, 7-10 cm long and fleshy splitting open into two halves when ripe (Peter, 2001). Nutmeg seeds grow from the fertilized female tree only. The average Nutmeg tree takes 9 years to mature. It needs extremely fertile soil and a temperature below 15.5 degrees Celsius.

Nutmeg should be kept in a dry cool place away from sunlight. It is better to buy whole nutmeg then grate them before usage. Mace should be stored in dry cool places away from sunlight, as well.
The name nutmeg came from 14th century "nux moschata" meaning musk-scented nut, and mace derived from the French word "maci," meaning "suitable for ointment"(Ellen, 1997).

Folklore:
Connecticut is known as the nutmeg state, because of the tradition of

slick Yankee peddlers selling carved wooden "nutmegs" to unsuspecting housewives.

Chemical structure:

Nutmeg and mace contains:
> Moisture;
> Volatile oil;
> Non-volatile ether;
> Starch;
> Sugars such as glucose and fructose;
> Total reducing sugars such as sucrose;
> Protein;
> Crude fibers;
> Ash;
> Polyphenols such as tannins.

The essential oil is highly sensitive to light and temperature and yields a pale yellowish or pale greenish oil.
However, nutmeg oil contains:
> Camphene;
> Limonene;
> Myrcene;
> Copaene;
> Safrole;
> Eugenol;
> Myristicin.

The major composition of both nutmeg and mace oils are monoterpene hydrocarbons, together with smaller amounts of oxygenated monoterpenes and aromatic ethers (Peter, 2001).

Main use:

Nutmeg is used in a variety of sweet and savory dishes, such as cakes, biscuits and seafood. It is particularly delicious in milk pudding and drinks such as mulled wine. Nutmeg is also particularly good with beef, stewed fruits, sauces, vegetables and Italian pastas. Mace is used in savory, and sweet dishes as well, and especially in milk-based recipes. It is added to seafood as well as cakes, and other desserts, soups, and poultry. It is used in processed meat such as sausages.

Though not the same flavor, mace and nutmeg may be used interchangeably. Store in glass jars in a dark place, such as the pantry.

Medicinal and functional properties:
Both nutmeg and mace are used in pharmaceutical industries.

1. The main constituents of nutmeg and mace (myristicin, elemicin and isoelimicin) when present as an aroma, act as stress relievers.
2. They have stimulative and carminative properties.
3. The seeds are carminative, stomachic, astringent, deodorant, narcotic, aphrodisiac and useful in flatulence, nausea, vomiting, helminthiasis, asthma, impotency, skin diseases, insomnia, fever and cardiac diseases (Warrier *et al.*, 1995).
4. Nutmeg has antioxidant properties.
5. Nutmeg butter is a mild external stimulant used in ointments, hair lotions and plaster.
6. Nutmeg butter is also used against mild rheumatism, paralysis and sprains.
7. Nutmeg oil is used in cosmetics and perfumes due to its aromatic properties.

Nutmeg was found to have antibacterial activity against *E. coli* O157 and *E. coli* O111 (Takikawa, 2002).

Toxicity:
Nutmeg is a common household spice, and excess use may be deliberate or inadvertent. It is difficult to diagnose nutmeg toxicity, as symptoms are non-specific. There are no biochemical markers of nutmeg use (Brendan *et al.*, 2003). Large doses produce toxicity and hallucinations and end in death (Ellen, 1997). There are some cases of nutmeg abuse dating from the 12th century (Shafran, 1976).

The psycho-activity of nutmeg is attributed to the fact that it is structurally similar to serotonin and antagonist like reserpine. Symptoms of toxicity usually manifest 6 hours after ingesting one whole nutmeg. Side effects and toxicity may range from tachycardia and flushing to central nervous system excitation. Psychiatric effects include hallucinations, delusions and psychosis (Brenner, 1993).

Chapter 15

Marjoram and Oregano:English
Marjoram: (Malayalam)
Murwa and Sathra: (Hindi)
Introduction:

Scientific Name: *Origanum majorana*
Scientific Name: *Origanum vulgare*
Family Name: Labiatae/Lamiaceae
Sweet marjoram is indigenous to Mediterranean countries and was
known to the ancient Egyptians, Greeks and Romans. Nowadays
marjoram is grown in central Germany, Hungary, southern France and
the USA.
Leaves are light, grayish-green, and oblate to broadly elliptical, margin
entire, reaching about 21 mm in length and 11 mm in breadth. The
flowers are small, white, pinkish or red (Duke, 1997).

The essential oil is very strong and of very pleasant fragrance. Sweet
marjoram is characterized by a strong spicy and pleasant odor.
Other species are: *wild marjoram* and *pot marjoram* (Peter, 2001).

Habitat:
Marjoram is a perennial plant with a height of 1- 3 feet and grows in
all kinds of soil and full sun, preferring rich soil. It may be stored in
the refrigerator for 3-4 days.

Oregano is a perennial that prefers well-drained, slightly alkaline soil
and full sun.

Religious importance and folklore:
It is believed marjoram should be added to all love charms and
sachets.

Marjoram is also known as Origanum, which is Greek for "mountain-joy." It was considered a favorite of Aphrodite. In ancient Greece it was believed that if you oint (apply) yourself with marjoram, you would have dreams of your future spouse.

Planting marjoram on a grave was believed to bring some comfort for the dead and ensure eternal peace and happiness. During ancient times, wreaths of marjoram crowned the heads of bridal couples to symbolize honor, love and happiness. Marjoram was used by Hippocrates as an antiseptic. During the Middle Ages, the leaves were often chewed to relieve toothache, rheumatism, indigestion and coughs. In ancient Egypt it was used for healing and disinfecting. Much of the marjoram referred to by the ancients was actually Oregano.

It is believed that Oregano can help one forget and let go of a former loved one, such as a former spouse, boyfriend, girlfriend, *etc*. It may be burnt in incenses or drunk in infusions to aid spells for letting go. Oregano is wild marjoram and has a stronger flavor. The English used oregano as an ingredient in snuff and as a perfume in sachets.

Chemical structure:
Marjoram is made of:
1. Monoterpenes: terpinolene, limonene, β-phellandrene, β - pinene, γ -terpinene, α -terpinene, camphene, ocimene.
2. Monoterpene alcohols: linalool, geraniol, trans-sabinene hydrate, borneol.
3. Monoterpene carbonyls: carvone, camphor.
4. Monoterpene esters: neral acetate, geranyl acetate, linalyl acetate and terpenyl-4-acetate.
5. Sesquiterpenes: farnesene, ledene, allo-aromadendrane.
6. Terpinoids ether/oxides: 1,8-cineol, aryophyllene epoxide.
7. Benzoidcompounds: p-ymene, eugenol, thymol, carvacrol, methyl chavicol and anethole.

Main use:
Fresh marjoram can either be used chopped or left whole. It has quite a delicate flavor. Marjoram leaves can be added during cooking, either just before the end or just before serving. It can be added to poultry, pork and fish dishes. It is also a complement to eggs and cheese dishes in Italian cuisines.

Oregano is an important herb used throughout Italy, generally used dried because of the enhanced flavor. Crush it between both palms before using to release its oils.

Poultry, meats, vegetables, vinaigrettes, and fish dishes in Italy and Greece are nicely enhanced with Oregano, and don't forget pizza!
Store dried Oregano in an airtight container on a pantry shelf.
Fresh Oregano may be frozen.

Medicinal value:

Marjoram herb is an effective cure for asthma coughs and is used to strengthen the stomach and intestines. It has several properties such as:

An antimicrobial;
An antioxidant ;
Control of platelets aggregation;
Anti-HIV activity;
Control of atopic eczema;
(Peter,2001).

Marjoram extract is used to give a gloss to dry hair and prevent hair loss (D'Amelio, 1999). It is useful for promoting perspiration, as a treatment for colds, flu, and fevers, to bring on menses and relieve associated menstrual discomfort, and to clear lungs and bronchial passages. Oregano has been found to exhibit antioxidant properties due to its phenolic content as well as rosmarinic acid content, which is the major phenolic component present in this type of Lamiaceae extracts (Dorman *et al.*, 2003).

To understand the mechanism, it must be understood that lipid peroxidation is a contradiction of aerobic life, affecting both human health and the quality of modern life (Davies *et al.*, 1995).

Shahidi tried to explain it by stating that "Biological systems are lipid-rich matrices susceptible to autoxidation unless protected by either endogenous enzymatic or non-enzymatic mechanisms". Antioxidants can act in several mechanisms, such as decomposing peroxides so that they cannot be reconverted to initiating active radicals (Shahidi *et al.*, 1992). Studies showed that Oregano contains 36% of phenols (Ollanketo *et al.*, 2002). Marjoram goes well with basil, which has a stronger flavor.

Chapter 16

Onion :English
Ulli, Chuvannulli : (Malayalam)
Pyaj : (Hindi)

Introduction:
Scientific Name: *Allium cepa*
Family Name: *Liliaceae*

The origin of the name "onion" derives from the classical Latin name "union," which means oneness or unity. The French call it oignon, which was created by adding the letter "o" to the Latin word, and then the letter "u" was dropped to create a modern spelling (Elcort, 1992). Onion is a famous spice grown all over the world and in various forms. The distinctive flavor of alliums has placed onions on a high "wanted" list in today's cuisine. It is used as immature or mature bulbs, as vegetable and spice, and as food for poultry and non-milking cattle.

Onion can be eaten raw or cooked; mild flavored or colored bulbs are often chosen for salads. Onions contain complex sulfur compounds. When you cut into an onion two chemical reactions take place. First when a knife cuts through the cells of an onion its enzyme releases a strong odor. Second, the onion releases allicin, a volatile sulfur gas that irritates the eyes and sends one rushing for a tissue.

There are different kinds of onions: cocktail, pearl, red, shallots, Spanish, spring, white and yellow.

Cocktail onions are tiny onions having a sweet white flesh and sold in pickles. Pearl onions are larger than pickling onions and have a sweet and delicate flavor. Pickling onions are main crop onions picked when still small; they are available only in autumn and have a pungent flavor. Red onions have a mild, sweet flavor and an attractive color. Shallots are not baby onions but a close relation. They have a mild flavor which is less overpowering than the most onions.

Spanish onions are onions that grow in warm climates, consequently they have a mild sweet flavor. Their skin has a golden color.

Spring onions are harvested at a very young age. They have small shoots and creamy white bulbs, both of which can be eaten.

White onions possess a strong pungent flavor with a distinctive white skin and flesh.

Finally, yellow onions are the most commonly used; they have a golden brown skin.

Habitat and storage:
Onions are cultivated mainly as biennial, but some types are perennials. They are found in 126 countries, mainly in the areas of Iran, Afghanistan, Pakistan and India. There are 325 species of onions, 70 of which grow in North America.

Cocktail onions should be kept in cool, dark places for up to one year. Pickling onions, which are available from September to November, should be kept in a cool, dark and airy place.
Red onions are available all year long and should also be stored in cool, dark and airy places.
Shallots, available all year long, should be kept in cool, dry places.
Spanish onions, available all year, should be stored in dark, cool and airy places.
Spring onions are only available from May to September and most be kept in the refrigerator for 3-4 days.
Finally, yellow onions need a dark and airy place (Potter and Hotchkiss, 1995).

History and folklore:
Onion has been eaten and cultivated since prehistoric times. It was mentioned in the first dynasty of ancient Egypt, circa 3200 BC; it was found in tomb paintings, inscriptions and documents from that time on. Of all the food in the plant kingdom, onions set the record for the most frequent appearance in ancient Egyptian art, often appearing as a sacrifice that appeared on their altars.

At that time in Egypt, an onion basket was considered a very respectable funeral offering.

Archeologists discovered small onions in the eye sockets in the mummy of King Ramses IV, who died in 1160 BC.

To Egyptians, the onion's concentric layers represented eternal life, and was buried with each of the Pharaohs. The Sumerians of Mesopotamia were the first to establish a written language, and archeologists found one of their inscriptions dating back to 2400 BC that read: " the oxen of the gods plowed the city governor's onion patches. The onion and cucumber patches of the city governor were located in the god's best field." Onions were so appreciated that Emperor Charlemagne ordered them to be planted in his royal garden. Further more, onions were even accepted as payment for the use of land.

"An old Turkish legend explains it: when Satan was thrown out of heaven, garlic sprouted where he first placed his foot and onions grew where he placed his right foot."

Chemical structure and Nutrition:

A common onion contains the following nutrient components:

> Moisture
> Protein
> CHO
> Ash
> Fat
> Ca, P, K, Na, Mg, Al, Ba, Fe, Sr, B, Cu, Zn, Mn, S.
> Vitamins: D, C
> Riboflavin,
> Pantothenic acid
> Folic acid
> Nicotinic acid (Peter, 2001).

Counting calories, sweet, raw onions have low caloric content. In half a cup of chopped raw onions there are 30 calories. If the same onions are cooked, they will be only up to 46 calories. Protein-wise, every half-cup contains around 1.4 grams. The fat content of the same quantity is around 0.1 grams for raw ones and 0.2 grams for those that are cooked.

The scallions used in our salads are very high in vitamin A, folic acids and vitamin C. They are also high in calcium, potassium and magnesium content.

Main use:
Though the onion has not yet distinguished itself in American cuisine, it has certainly in other countries. The British love stuffed onions. The French created an onion soup which turned out to become a universal favorite, and also developed the gourmet onion. India developed onion fritters.

Onion skins are usually considered the discard of the vegetable, but not always. Some have discovered its powerful ability to lend a rich, golden color to soups and to dye yarn and fabric. Greeks traditionally use red onion skins to dye their Easter eggs a bright pinkish red. Each kind of onion can be used in a certain specific dish. For instance, Cocktail onions should be pickled and added to a selection of cold meats or eaten with crusty bread. Pearl onions can be added to stews and casseroles or fried in a little oil or butter with a little vinegar and then added to roasted meat. Pickling onions should first be preserved in vinegar and then left to mature; thereafter they can be served with cheese and cold meats. Red onions are used as garnishes or combined with tomatoes and red leaf lettuce for salads; they can also be served with cold entrees or fried with oil. And yellow onions are used in a variety of dishes, from casseroles, pies and quiches to stir-fries, sauces and pizzas.

Medicinal and functional properties:
Besides use as a condiment and spice for flavoring and enriching various cuisines, onion has been known for its high medicinal properties:

It acts as a stimulant, diuretic and expectorant, and mixed with vinegar it is useful for a sore throat. Essential oil from onion contains a heart stimulant, and increases pulse volume and frequency of systolic pressure and coronary flow (Duke, 1997).

Onion consumption lowers blood sugar, lipids and cholesterol. Two to three slices of onions can be a cure for the measles. Fresh onion juice has antibacterial properties due to allicin, disulfide and cysteine compounds and their interactions.

Anti-platelets aggregation effects in human and animal blood has been reported after regular consumption of onion (Peter, 2001). In Chinese medicine, globe onions are used to calm the liver, moisten the intestines and benefit the lungs. Raw onions are prescribed for constipation, lowering high blood pressure and for healing wounds or ulcers of the skin. Spring onions, or scallions, are used to induce sweating. One remedy for the common cold is to take 20 spring onions and simmer them with rice to make porridge; add vinegar and eat them warm. At the University of California, researchers found that yellow and red onions contain quercitin, which is a powerful antioxidant that acts as an anti-cancer agent to block the formation of cancer cells. About 1.5 to 3.5 oz of raw onions eaten regularly contain enough quercetin to offer cancer protection. Selenium, which is a trace element of onions, has also demonstrated anti-cancer abilities (Mahan, 2003).

It was also found that quercitin deactivates the growth of estrogen-sensitive cells often found to cause breast cancer. Asthma sufferers may also benefit from a hearty dose of onions. There is a sulfur compound in onions that can prevent the biochemical chain reaction that leads to asthma attacks (Duke, 1997). Onion can be used as an aphrodisiac. It can also be useful in hemorrhoids, dysentery, flatulence, colic, jaundice, malarial fever, lumbago, epilepsy leucoderma and skin diseases (Warrier *et al.*, 1994).

Peeling without tears:

Historically, the onion is nothing to cry about. Over many centuries it occupied an exalted position as a work of art as well as food. Few people today would burst into tears if they were asked to consider the onion as a work of art, but they might do so if they had to peel one raw. Many techniques for preventing tears can be used while peeling an onion, such as holding a lit match between the teeth, and peeling and chopping the onions under running water, but these might not always be convenient. The most successful way is to put the onion in the refrigerator until it is quite cold. This method has a chilling effect on the volatile sulfur oils.

Chapter 17

Rosemary and Sage: English
Sugantha chedi: (Malayalam)
Rusmari : (Hindi)
A . Rosemary

Introduction:
Scientific Name: *Rosmarinus officinalis*
Family Name: *Lamiaceae*
Rosemary is a bushy, branched shrub attaining a height of 1 meter. It bears aromatic, evergreen, opposite, sessile, linear pale blue flowers.
Its leaves are 1.5-3.5 cm long and 2.2 cm wide (D'Amelio, 1999).
Rosemary is one of the most valuable spices, widely used in food processing. It is the only spice commercially available for use as an antioxidant.

The most effective component of the plant is: Rosmaric acid, its structure elucidated as an ester of caffeic acid and 3, 4-dihydroxy-phenyllactic acid (Scarpati and Oriente, 1958). The caffeic acid is made only of phenylalanine and the 3,4-dihydroxyphenyllactic acid of tyrosine (Ellis and Towers, 1970).

Habitat:
Rosemary is a perennial that prefers mild climates available inside the house. It reaches a height of 2-4 feet and tolerates poor soils.
It grows in Mediterranean regions.

Religious importance:
It is believed that Rosemary is used for protection from evil spirits and any harm that may happen to a person. It is considered the herb of fidelity. It you sprinkle some around the house it may bring good luck and protection. Students in ancient Greece wore garlands of Rosemary around their necks or braided Rosemary into their hair to improve their memory during exams.

Rosemary has been used at weddings and funerals, and even to ward off the plague. In Hamlet, Ophelia said "there's Rosemary, that's for resemblance". It has a strict association with beauty. According to legend, Rosemary was used to awaken Sleeping Beauty.

Chemical composition:

Rosemary is made of: essential oil, rosmarinic acid, proteins, tannins, borneol, boron, diosmin, camphor, flavonoids, phenolic acids and triterpenic acid.The main components are: 1,8-cineole, camphor, α-pinene, β-pinene, β-caryophyllene, camphene, borneol, α-terpineol, bornyl acetate, myrcene, and terpinen-4-ol (Clarke, 2002).

Main use:

Rosemary, its great flavor, is prevalent in Italian cooking. It is traditionally used with roast lamb meats and chicken, vegetables and breads. It is also popular in marinades and casseroles, and used with fish in hot barbecue. Fresh Rosemary can be added to certain dishes and removed before cooking, flavoring the dish with a nice smell and taste.

Rosemary flavored oil is also popular, as is Rosemary flavored vinegar. The flavor of Rosemary will become overpowering if the dish is not sufficiently degreased. It is a sturdy herb that needs to be chopped before use. Whole leaves may be laid on roasting meats, discarding after the cooking time, Fresh Rosemary will last only a few days in the refrigerator, so plan for quick usage.

Medicinal and functional properties:

Rosemary stimulates the circulatory system and treats bites and stings. It is also used as well as a hair restorer (externally).
Rosemary treats migraines, bad breath, stimulates sexual organs, treats nervous disorders, upset stomachs, regulates menstrual cycle and eases cramps (internally).
Rosmarinic acid, found in Rosemary plants, has a number of important biological values such as:

      Antiviral;
      Antibacterial;
      Anti-inflammatory;

Antioxidative;

Antimutagen;

Astrigent (Parnham and Kesselring, 1985).

It is also used for arthritis, baldness, depression, fainting and wrinkles (Duke, 1997).

Due to its phenolic component, the Rosemary plant was also found to provide protection against cancer (Peterson and Simmonds, 2003).In addition, it has been used in the cosmetic industry and for cleaning old ulcers and wounds.

Toxicity:

Prolonged exposure to the concentrated liquid and vapor may be very irritating for the skin, with a possible irritation of the eyes.

B. Sage

Scientific Name: *Salvia spp.*
Family Name: *Lamiaceae.*

Sage is a perennial, short-shrub one foot high. Its flowers start appearing in the early summer, and can be blue, pink or even white followed by black nut lets (D'Amelio, 1999).

Sage is used in foods for flavoring and seasoning. It has a strong, aromatic and slightly bitter taste.

Sage, along with Rosemary, possess the highest antioxidant property.

Habitat:
Sage is a perennial evergreen growing best in sandy, limey soil and full sun. It is found in Mediterranean regions and southern Europe.

Religious importance:

It is believed that Sage used in amulets can be healing, and it may be responsible for bringing wealth, prosperity, richness and fame to people who keep this herb with them. In Roman times, Sage was associated with strength and power as well as with the straight functioning of the brain and intelligence.

During the Middle Ages, Sage was used as a healing herb to treat fevers and epilepsy, memory loss, eye problem and intestinal problems. Charlemagne had it grown in his royal garden.

Chemical composition:

Sage is made of: volatile oil, thujone, borneol, linalool, camphors, pinene, estrogenic compounds, salvin, carnosolic acid, caryophyllene, proteins, beta-sitosterol, saponins, flavonoids, phenolic acids and tannins (D'Amelio, 1999).

Main use:
Sage is often used with pork and goose.
The whole leaves can be served with meat dishes when deep fried. Sage's leaves can be chopped, depending on what they are going to be used for.

Sage can be used in cheeses, sausages and food stuffing such as for chicken or pork. It is used with butter in many dishes such as Italian pastas.

It is also used in the Mediterranean diet along with meat and cooked vegetables. It is used as a dry component to dissipate bad odors and unwanted flavors, and remains unchanged when frozen.

Medicinal and functional properties:
Sage relieves excess mucous buildup, eases mental exhaustion, strengthens concentrating abilities, treats sores and skin eruptions, stops bleeding in all cuts, soothes mouth sores and sore throats. It can be used for all stomach troubles, such as diarrhea, gas, flu, and colds. It is used to regulate the menstrual cycle, to affect milk flow in lactating women, and as a deodorant (Peter, 2001).

Beauty wise, Sage has been found to give dark hair its natural color. If hair is massaged with Sage, dandruff will be removed and hair loss controlled.

Chapter 18

Saffron :English
Kesar: (Hindi)
Kumkumappuvu: (Malayalam)

Introduction:
Scientific Name: *Crocus sativus*
Family Name: *Iridaceae*

Saffron is the most expensive spice in the world, as it is extracted from the dry stigmata of the *saffron crocus*. It takes thousands of stigmas to produce just 25 g of saffron. The dried stigmas contain a coloring substance which gives a musty, honey flavor and a bright yellow color to rice or anything else it is added to. Saffron is available in powder or strands. Both forms should be stored in a cool, dry place away from direct sunlight (Peter, 2001).

Habitat:
Saffron is a perennial and prefers well-drained soil with plenty of water and sun. It originated from Asian Minor and is cultivated now in Spain, Austria, Italy, Greece, Iran and Kashmir. At one time, saffron was extensively cultivated in England.

Religious importance:
It is believed that Saffron cleanses the hands before rituals, heals when used in mixtures and is an essential oil used to induce clairvoyance (sensory contact).

Chemical structure:
In ancient times, saffron was an important dye, but nowadays it is mainly used in cooking and food processing. The major components responsible for the strong, effective, agreeable color of saffron are cis and trans crocins, which are rare water-soluble carotenoids. The molecular formula of the most common crocin is $C_{44}H_{64}O_{24}$. Crocins, have also been found in the plant: *Gardenia jasminoides,* which *is* a small white flower having an amazingly agreeable smell. In addition, saffron also contains the flavonoids derivatives, picrocrocin and its

aglaycone safranal, in lower quantities. Picrocrocin is responsible for the bitter taste of saffron and is being developed as a food additive (Li et al., 1999).

Main use:

Saffron has a bitter flavor and yellow color; it is best used in acidic dishes.

Indian saffron is really turmeric, and American saffron is really safflower.

Saffron threads are preferred over ground saffron.

Turmeric is a viable substitute for saffron.

Saffron must be stored away from sunlight and kept in an airtight container.

It should be purchased in small quantities as the flavor dissipates quickly. Use sparingly, as it is very expensive and very powerful, just a few grains may change the color of whole food.

Always use less than you might think as it might overpower the dish.

Saffron powder can be added directly to food, however saffron strands should be introduced first in warm water then added with their liquid to the meals at the end of cooking.

Many traditional foods include saffron, such as: saffron bread and saffron cake.

It is widely used in Mediterranean countries, used in chicken, shellfish and rice dishes. It is also an essential constituent of the Spanish paella.

Medicinal value:

Several health benefits are associated with this plant, such as:

Prevention of heart disease;

Prevention of cholesterol build-up;

Soothing of the membranes of the stomach and colon;

Inhibiting cell growth of human tumor cells;

Easing digestive disorders;

Cancer therapeutic agents;

Anodyne;

       Anti hysteric;

       Antiseptic;

       Antispasmodic;

       Aphrodisiac;

       Balsamic;

       Cardiotonic;

Carminative;
Ecbolic;
Diaphoretic;
Emmenagogue;
Expectorant;
Nervine;
Stimulant;
Useful in menstrual disorders and strengthening of the heart;
Reducing inflammation.

Pregnant women should not take it. Several studies have shown cells to be sensitive to saffron and its components. Differences in sensitivity to saffron and its main ingredients in normal and malignant cells could be due to the existence of receptors found on the surface of the cell, intracellular retention transport, differences in the uptake of certain drugs or in the methods used for the extraction of toxicity. It was also demonstrated that the saffron extract inhibited cellular nucleic acid synthesis and had no effect on protein synthesis in tumor cells (Nair and Hasegawa, 1995).

Interestingly, there was a stimulatory or supporting effect of the saffron extract on the non-specific proliferation of lymphocytes *in vitro* and on colony formation of normal human lung cells. Characteristic compounds of saffron include crocin, safranal, picrocrocin, crocetin and α-carotene. It was shown that these saffron ingredients inhibited different types of tumor cell growth, although it had a dose-dependent inhibitory effect on DNA, RNA and protein synthesis of different human malignant cells (Escribano *et al.,*1996). It was recently shown that saffron corms contain several components acting against tumor cells (Escribano *et al.,* 1996).

Chapter19

Tamarind: *(English)*
Kolpuli, Valanpuli: (Malayalam)
Imli, Amli : (Hindi)

Introduction:
ScientificName:*Tamarindus indica*
FamilyName:*Caesalpiniaceae*

The tamarind tree is one of the most important multipurpose tree species in the Indian sub-continent. It is a large evergreen tree with a beautiful, spreading crown (Peter, 2001). The inconspicuous, inch-wide, five-petalled flowers are born in small racemes and are yellow with orange or red steaks. The flower buds are pink, due to the outer color of the four sepals, which are shed when the flower opens. The tamarind fruit pulp has been an important ingredient in India for a very long period. It is 3-8 inches long, brown, and irregularly curved pods grow in abundance along the branches. When the pods are mature, they are filled out. When fully ripe, the shells are brittle and easily broken. The pulp has a sweet/sour flavor and has a very high acidic and sugar content (Morton, 1987). It is mostly found in central and south India states and also in southeast Asian countries. The pulpy portion of the seed is used mainly as an acidulant in Indian recipes (Marathe *et al.*, 2002).

New habitat and adaptation:
Tamarinds are slow-growing, long-living evergreen trees that under optimum conditions can grow to 80 feet high with a spread of 30 feet. The tamarind is well adapted to semiarid tropical conditions, even though it can tolerate humid, tropical are as with high rainfall. Young trees are very susceptible to frost but mature trees can with stand 28 degree Fahrenheit with no damage. Dry weather is important for fruit development. They are found in Africa, Asia and southern California (Popenoe,1974).

History:
The tamarind is native to tropical Africa and grows wild in Sudan. It was introduced into India so long ago. It is extensively cultivated in tropical areas of the world. During the sixteenth century, it was introduced into America, and today it is widely grown in Mexico, as well.

Chemical composition: Several oligosaccharides can be isolated from the tamarind fruit (Mazz *et al.*, 2003). It is made of citric acid, tartaric acid, malic acid, potassium, bitartrate, gum, pectin, some grape sugar and parenchymatous fiber.

Mainuse:
Tamarind, also known as Indian date, possesses a sour flavor. It is a very important and tasty constituent when used along with fish and chicken, curries, chutneys, rice and lentils. Tamarind is best purchased as a concentrate, as so little is needed and so much preparation is required before the seeds can be used. It should be stored in an airtight container on the pantry shelf or in the refrigerator. Tarragon vinegar gives an excellent flavor to vinaigrettes, marinades and is used to flavor many prepared mustards. Store fresh leaves in plastic containers in the refrigerator. If the leaves are left exposed to the sun, they will not have the same properties as when quick-frozen, since the essential oils present will rapidly deteriorate.

Tamarind's wood is very hard and durable, thus valuable for building purposes and furnishing excellent charcoal for gunpowder; the leaves give a yellow dye. Tamarind is used to prepare ready-to-eat jelly formulations. It is used in many products such as jams, jellies, marmalades, and preserves. It is used as a sauce for many delicious platters with goose, duck and water fowl. In addition, it is added to confectionary, salad dressings and mayonnaise; as well as frozen desserts such as ice cream, ice milk, and sherbet. Tamarind seeds have been used to prepare gum solutions (Veluraja *et al.*, 1997).

Medicinal and Functional properties:
Medicinal values have been found for several preparations, including the fruit, leaves, flowers and bark. Tamarind has many functional properties, such as:

Diuretic;
Antiscorbutic;
Astringent;
Febrifuge;
Antiseptic;
Cathartic;
Refrigerant.
Laxative action: The pulp is a good part of the diet in convalescence for maintaining a slightly laxative action of the bowels;
Cooling fevers;
Fighting swellings and boils;
Delaying progression of fluorosis by enhancing urinary excretion of fluoride (Khandar *et al.*, 2002);
Relieving pain;
Correction of bilious disorders;
Anti-inflammatory functions. Preserving salty fishes (Peter, 2001);
In addition tamarind root bark is astringent, constipating and useful in diarrhea, gingivitis and asthma;
Tamarind leaves are anthelmintic, anodyne, antifugal.

Leaves are also used to treat jaundice, scabies, tumors, ringworm, boils, smallpox, otalgia and conjunctivitis, alcoholic intoxication and Datura poisoning. The seeds are used as an astringent, aphrodisiac and stomachic (Warrier *et al.*, 1996). Nowadays, tamarind extracts (TKP) are purified and refined and used as thickening, stabilizing and gelling agent in the food industry. The polysaccharide present in tamarind has the ability to form gel in the presence of sugar or alcohol. It has the same properties as the fruit pectin (Marathe *et al.*, 2002).

Chapter 20

Turmeric: *(English)*
Manchal: *(Malayalam)*
Haldi: *(Hindi)*

Introduction:
Scientific Name: *Curcuma domestica*
or *Curcuma longa*
Family Name: *Zingeberaceae*

Turmeric grows in curved or partially-straight cylindrical branches, having a tapered end. Its branches are hard and heavy; they can break with a short fracture. The useful part of this plant is the dried rhizome, which is used in curry powder or raw in chicken bouillon, gravies, dry seasonings, baking mixes, processed cheese, pickles and beverages. Turmeric is a perennial herb found in rich soils, wooded areas of northern New Jersey (Cecil, 1998). It is grown as an annual crop. It is native to southern Asia and is cultivated in India, China, Java and other tropical countries. India is the major producer and exporter of turmeric in the world.

Traditional use:
Turmeric is used in India in various religious ceremonies and in Indonesia in wedding ceremonies to dye the arms of the bride and bridegroom. In Java boys who are undergoing circumcision ceremonies are covered with it. Buddhists use Turmeric to dye their robes to get the characteristic orange color. From Ancient times in India and southeast Asia it became known as the "Salt of the Orient"(Ellen, 1997). Turmeric is a necessary ingredient in curry powder. It is used extensively in Indian dishes, including lentil and meat dishes, and in southeast Asian cooking. Turmeric is routinely added to mustard blends and relishes. It can replace saffron, as it provides a similar taste and color.

Chemical structure:
Turmeric is made up of 3-5 % yellow pigments, not volatile and made

of curcumin, monodesmethoxycurcumin, and bisdesmethoxycurcumin. It also contains 2-7 % essential oil that includes bisabolane, guaiane and germacrane sesquiterpenes: tumerone, ar-turmerone, zingiberene, and curlone. Starch that is largely gelatinized and ukonan A are also present in this plant (D'Amelio, 1999).

Taste and Aroma:
Turmeric is mildly aromatic with scents of orange or ginger. It has a pungent, bitter flavor.

Main use:
Turmeric has an appearance similar to ginger and is in fact, a member of that family, being the rhizome of the same plant. It is a warm flavored spice that is used in cuisine. It is one of the spices that comprise cooking powder.

Turmeric adds a yellow color to the dish you are preparing. Turmeric is terrific in curries, chutneys, rice, and potato dishes as well as meat and seafood dishes. In a small amount, Turmeric may be used as a substitute for saffron. The bright yellow color will be present but the flavor slightly altered, as Turmeric is milder and gives a stronger taste. Turmeric should be stored away from light in an airtight container.

Turmeric stains can be washed out with soap and water if treated quickly. Use Turmeric to add Eastern mystery to new platters as well as in traditional curries, rice and chicken dishes.

Turmeric is a classic addition to chutneys, pickles, and relishes. A pinch of Turmeric can be added to fish soups, and it can be blended with melted butter and drizzled over cooked vegetables, pasta, or potatoes (Duke, 2001). As Turmeric stains clothes and fingers it should be handled carefully.

Medicinal and functional properties:
Turmeric has many important properties such as:

  Antioxidant;
  Anti-inflammatory;
  Anti-arthritis;

Anti-edemic;
Choleretic;
Hypotensive;
Antibacterial and antifungal;
Antimutagenic (D'Amelio, 1999).

Turmeric also works as an appetizer, carminative, stomachic, anthelmintic, laxative, diuretic, expectorant, haematinic. It can be used for ulcers, wounds, leprosy, pruritus, allergic conditions, anorexia, dyspepsia, flatulence, colic, asthma, bronchitis, hemorrhages, haepatomegaly, splenomegaly, fever, giddiness, elephantiasis, epilepsy, ringworm, jaundice and for diabetes (Warrier *et al.*, 1994). It also reduces blood clotting and liver toxins. It helps in weight loss and is also used for cobra bite poisoning. In India Turmeric is used by women to remove facial and body hair by applying as a paste with milk, as well as to add a golden color to their faces. In India it is also used in the preparation of different perfumery (Ellen, 1997).

Curcumin is the ingredient responsible for the yellow color of Turmeric. It alters the function of nuclear factor kB and inhibits angiogenesis.

Many studies have shown that curcumin increases tumor cell apoptosis, decreases cell growth rate and reduces the number of clonogenic cells in a dose-dependent manner.

Curcumin is greatly utilized because of its low toxicity and strong antioxidant activity (Kerr, 2002).

Chapter 21

Green tea: English

Teyila : (Malayalam)

Chai : (Hindi)

Introduction:
Scientific Name: *Camellia sinensis,* various sp.
Family Name: *Theaceae*

Temperate climates are the best places to find the Green Tea plant. The content of caffeine, polyphenols and threonine characterizes its specific taste. One of the most important processes in tea manufacturing for drinks is fermentation, which is the conversion of the tannins in the leaves. The degree of fermentation will give us several types of drinkable tea, which are classified into: unfermented tea, which is nothing but green tea; semi-fermented: the oo-long tea, and finally, the fully-fermented tea known as black tea. Although the three types of tea are derived from the same plant specie, there are two major varieties of tea plant that are distinguished due to the leaf size. If one ingests black tea for its polyphenols content, it would be better to ingest green tea, as it has a higher polyphenols content (Mitscher and Victoria, 1998).

Religious importance:
Green tea has been used in rituals performed for wealth and to honor deities around the world. Since ancient times, green tea has been prized as a traditional tonic for keeping the body and soul in good condition.

Habitat:
This herb can grow in various temperate climates around the world. It flourishes best in areas with foggy mornings, balmy days of 65 degrees

Fahrenheit and heavy yearly rainfalls.

The plant needs an acidic soil, making sedimentary soils are the best milieu for it. It is cultivated mainly in China, Japan, India and Sri Lanka (Mitscher and Victoria, 1998).

Chemical composition:

The major component of green tea is carbohydrates (cellulose) and proteins that are almost insoluble components. It also contains tea polyphenols, caffeine, amino acids, vitamins, inorganic elements and lipids.

a. Tea polyphenols:

Polyphenols are naturally occurring compounds that gives the tea its pungency and unique flavor. The unoxidised polyphenols in green tea are responsible for its subtle color and astringency (Mitscher and Victoria,1998).Green tea leaves contain six kinds of polyphenols, but the most important ones are Catechins and Gallic acid. Those polyphenols have demonstrated many properties, such as:

> Antimutagenic activity;
> Suppressive effect of chromosome aberration;
> Antioxidant activity (Gilbert, 1984);
> Depressor effect on renal hypertension;
> Inhibitory effect on arteriosclerosis (Penny *et al.*, 2002);
> Inhibitory effect on lipid peroxidation.

b. Caffeine:

Very few tea plants contain caffeine. Caffeine is a trimethyl derivative of purine 2,6-diol and is mainly found in tea plants.
It has many functions, such as:

> Cardiac stimulant;
> Diuretic;
> Stimulant of the cerebral cortex causing excitation (Jarvis, 1993);
> Doubling endurance in sports. Coffee increases the free fatty acids level (which is used as an energy source in the body), while sparing the body the glycogen reserve (Lamarine, 1994).

However, high doses of caffeine have side effects, such as:

> Muscle tension;
> Nausea;
> Nervousness;
> Sleepiness;
> Irritation of the gastro intestinal tract (GI tract) (Mitscher and Victoria,1998);
> Increase in blood cholesterol level due to the cafestol component.

c. Amino acids:

The main free amino acids found in tea are: Threonine (45.9%), Glutamic acid (12.7%), Arginine (9.2%), Aspartic acid (10.8%), Glutamine (7.5%), Serine, Threonine, Alanine, Asparagine, and Lysine. Their presence has a preventive effect on increase in blood pressure.

d. Vitamins:

Commercial green tea contains high amounts of vitamin C (280 mg in 100 g of dried green tea). However, we find lesser amounts in oo-long tea and black tea, since they are more processed (fermented) than the green tea which is not fermented at all, and vitamin C is very highly volatile upon heating (100%). The presence of Vitamin C protects against scurvy and colds. Other vitamins, such as B2, D, K and the carotenoids are present in Green Tea, as well (Mitscher and Victoria, 1998).

e. Inorganic elements:

Green tea is very high in inorganic elements, such as:
(These contents are per 100 g of green tea).

> Nitrogen -3.5-7.1 g;
> Potassium- 0.2-0.7 g;
> Magnesium- 0.12-0.3 g;
> Iron- 100-200 ppm;
> Sodium -20-33 ppm;
> Copper -15-20 ppm;
> Selenium -1.0-1.8 ppm;
> Aluminum - 420-3500 ppm;
> Fluorine- 17-260 ppm (Fulder, 1998).

It has been found that the tea plant has a biochemical mechanism to neutralize the toxicity of aluminum by storing it in tea leaves as chelates ; this is the role of the polyphenols (Drewitt *et al.*, 1993). Fluorine has shown beneficial properties such as preventing bacterial attack on teeth; however, since tea is roasted at such a high temperature, it forms an inactive complex: the aluminum fluoride is ineffective against dental caries.

f. Carbohydrates:
The carbohydrate content of green tea is 40%, from which one third is cellulose fiber beneficial for digestion.

g. Lipids:
Found in 4% of the leaves from which 14% are in the form of saturated fatty acids and 86% in the form of unsaturated fatty acids, such as oleic and linoleic acid (Fulder, 1998).

Medicinal and functional properties:
This herb is an effective anti-oxidant and reduces the risk of many forms of cancer. It has the ability to stabilize blood lipids, aiding in treating high cholesterol and hypertension, and stimulate immune functions. Green tea also eases mental fatigue and lowers the risks for arteriosclerosis and strokes. In addition, the leaves act as a carminative diuretic, diaphortic and nerve tonic, and is useful in opthalmia, hemorrhoids, inflammations, abdominal disorders, fever and fatigue (Warrier *et al.*, 1994).

Most of these properties are due to the presence of polyphenolic components in the green tea leaves. Most of the functional properties of this herb are listed below:

1. Protection against cardiovascular disease:
One of the most important discoveries is that green tea is able to increase the heart's resistance to cardiovascular diseases. Consuming high quantities of green tea means a high consumption of polyphenols, leading to a reduction of heart attacks. This drink also protects the blood vessels, leading to 75% fewer strokes in men. From the cholesterol point of view, a person drinking eight or nine cups of green tea per day has a relatively lower cholesterol level (lower LDL) (Kono

et al., 1992). Not only is the LDL decreased but the HDL will be increased as well (HDL is the good cholesterol) this will lead to a protection against triglycerides. Green tea has been found to reduce platelets aggregation, or thinning the blood (decreasing by this process the risk of having a stroke) and a reduction in blood pressure (Sagesaka-Mitane *et al.,* 1990).

2. Acting as a digestive aid:

Once ingested, green tea polyphenols enter the intestinal tract and make their way throughout the body (He and Kies, 1994). They meddle with the carbohydrate metabolism by inhibiting the function of Amylase the enzyme of the saliva that starts the digestion of sugars in the mouth which diminishes the absorption of glucose derived from complex carbohydrates (Liu *et al.,* 1995).

In addition, polyphenols inhibit the activity of sucrase and glucosidase, which are the essential enzymes for the digestion of carbohydrate in the small intestine. (Honda and Hara, 1993). Finally, green tea alters the mechanism by which glucose passes through the intestinal wall. All these functions are beneficial for low glucose content in blood making green tea very helpful in diabetes and obesity (Matsumoto *et al.,* 1993). Green tea does not interfere with iron absorption, but the opposite: it resolves iron-deficiencies in the body (Mitamura *et al.,* 1989). Green tea promotes a healthy digestive tract by making the intestines a healthy environment for the growth of friendly bacteria and inhibiting the growth of harmful bacteria. In addition, green tea increases the regularity of bowel movement. Finally, people consuming green tea were found to have reduced odor from the feces (Terada *et al.,* 1993).

3. Antioxidative activity on fats and oils:

Green tea polyphenols have been shown to posses a suppressive effect on the oxidation of oil, and this effect is concentration dependent. This inhibitory effect leads to a minimal rancid development in oils and edible fats (Fulder, 1998).

4. Anti-discoloring effects:

Green tea has been found very effective in acting against discoloration by UV lights.

5. Antioxidant property:

Green tea has shown anti-oxidative activity *in vitro* as well as *in vivo*. Hence it can prevent living cells from oxidative impairment. This antioxidant property helps in the protection of the skin from free radicals, therefore lessening the likelihood of wrinkles (Makimura *et al.*, 1993).

6. Chemopreventive effect on carcinogenesis:

Based on several epidemiological studies, it was shown that green tea polyphenols have very beneficial effects in reducing cancer risks. Green tea polyphenols act against oxidative radicals that can damage DNA. They react with electrophilic carcinogenic species to form polyphenol-carcinogen adduct, that may result in the prevention of tumor formation. They inhibit the growth of intestinal clostridia. They inhibit biochemical signals of tumor initiation and promotion (Fulder, 1998). Drinking one to two cups of green tea per day decreases the risk of cancer by 10% (Zheng *et al.*, 1992).

7. Suppressive effect of uremic toxin formation:

Green tea polyphenols suppress the formation of uremic toxin (methylguanidine) and thus improves renal function.

8. Prevention of dental caries:

Green tea contains high concentrations of fluorides, which show strong inhibition for glycan synthesis (Sato and Niwa, 1995). Rinsing the teeth with green tea helps reduce the deposition of cavity-promoting plaques. The polyphenolic content of green tea helps in the inhibition of *Streptococcus mutans,* the bacteria responsible for plaque deposition (Ooshima *et al.*, 1993).

In addition, green tea has shown many additional properties, such as:
Antiviral effects;
Anti-inflammatory effects, by inhibiting the release of histamine from cells and lowering the release of allergy-mediated chemicals in the body (Ohmori *et al.*, 1995);
Treatment of diarrhea;
Antimicrobial properties;
Protection against osteoporosis, by reducing the excessive re - absorption that could lead to an excess loss in bone mass (Delaisse *et al.*, 1986);
Deodorizing effect (Duke, 1997).

Chapter 22

Licorice: English
Erattimadhuram : (Malayalam)
Mulhathi : (Hindi)

Introduction:
Scientific Name: *Glycyrrhiza glabra*
Family Name: *Fabaceae*
Synonyms: **Sweet wood, Glycyrrhia, Liquiritral Radix.**

Licorice is made of a dried rhizome, roots and a leguminous plant with pinnate leaves and spikes of blue flowers (Foster, 1999). Its sweetness is due to the presence of glycyrrhizin compound, a saponin glycoside that is present in the plant root at a concentration of 5-9%. The taste of licorice and aniseed are very similar, but the two plants do not possess the same functional properties. Licorice extracts are used in flavoring tobacco products.

Religious importance:
It is believed that Licorice root was buried in tombs and caskets to help the soul pass easily into the Summerland. A piece of Licorice root, when chewed, makes a person passionate. The root has been used to lengthen lifespan, for improving health, alleviating injury and for swelling and detoxification purposes in China (Nomura and Fukai, 1998). In Rome, the root was also used for diseases of the stomach, liver and kidney (Shibata, 2000).

Habitat:
This plant is perennial; it reaches 3 to 7 feet tall and grows best in warm, sunny climates. It is found mostly in central and western Asia, southern Europe, Russia and Hungary, and is cultivated in Japan and China.

Chemistry:
Triterpene glycoside is the basic active constituent of Licorice Root. Glycyrrhizin, which is found in a concentration of 2-20%, is the main

component.

When hydrolised, this glycyrrhizin produces glycyrrhetic acid and glucoronic acid.

Licorice also contains as well flavonoids, isoflavonoids (licoflavonol, glabrol, licoricone), chalcones, such as isoliquiritigenin and echinatin, coumarins and finally, lignin, amino acids, amines, gum wax and sterols (D'Amelio, 1999).

Licorice is also made up of alkaloids, amino acids, dihydrophenanthrenes, dihydrostilbenes, essential oils, fatty acids, polysaccharides and saponins (Nomura and Fukai, 1998).

Medicinal value:
The roots and stolons of some *Glycyrrhiza* species that have been used for medicinal purposes for more than 4000 years are referred to as "Licorice".
These plants contain a high amount of isoprenoids, substituted flavonoids (Nomura and Fukai, 1998).
These flavonoid-rich fractions from the extract of Licorice have been utilized as anti-ulcer (Takagi and Ishii, 1967).
The herb is a major source of the female hormone estrogen.
It is used for many purposes, such as:
> Treating cough and chest ailments;
> Treating stomach and heart problems;
> Treating indigestion and most respiratory ailments;
> Relieving peptic ulcer pain .
It is also:
> Good for skin eruptions;
> Anti-inflammatory;
> Antibacterial;
> Antiseptic;
> Antiviral;
> Antiphlogistic;
> Expectorant;
> An excellent taste for masking nauseous medicines;
> (D'Amelio, 1999).

In addition, the root of Liquorice is diuretic, a mild laxative and aphrodisiac, and promotes intellect. According to Warrier *et al.*,(1995), a decoction of the root is a good wash for falling out and graying of hair.

Licorice is the most used crude drug in Kampo medicines. The extract of the medicinal plant is also used as the basis of several anti-ulcer medicines, such as for the treatment of peptic ulcer.

Among the different chemical constituents of the plant, only glabridin, glabrene, licoricidin and licochalcone revealed inhibitory activity against the growth of *Helicobacter pylori*. These flavonoids revealed anti-*H. pylori* activity against a clarithromycin and amoxicillin resistant strain (Fukai *et al.*, 2002). Glycyrin, formononetin and isolicoflavonol may be useful chemopreventive agents for peptic ulcers or gastric cancer in *H. Pylori*- infected individuals. *Helicobacter pylori* is a bacterium that resides in the stomach and duodenum and is classified as one of the major causes of peptic ulcer. Therefore, ulcer patients need an antimicrobial treatment in addition to anti-secretory drugs, whether it is their first bout or a recurrence (Gorden *et al.*, 1994).

Developing countries such as Japan and Russia are having a rise in the number of patients infected with cancer and especially gastric cancer, although it is relatively uncommon in western nations (Marshal and Warren, 1984). Gastric cancer and peptic ulcer have been found to be related. Licorice is considered a chemopreventive agent for many diseases. The root of Licorice is very rich in flavonoids and is used for the treatment of gastritis and gastric ulcer as a prescribed drug, Licorice extracts are utilized in drugs for gastritis, gastric ulcer and duodenal ulcer, as well, and also as stomachic, cough medicine and a chemopreventive agent for side-effects of other medicines.

Licorice and its extracts are prescribed as bronchial remedies, gastrointestinal remedies, liver and bile remedies and urological remedies in western countries (Willuhn, 1994). Licorice has been found to be effective in the treatment of gastritis, ulcer, hemorrhoids, melanoma, and food poisoning.

Among all the Liquorice constituents, glycyrrhizin was the most active in inhibiting replication of the SARS-associated virus (Cinatl *et al.*, 2003).

The mechanism described by Jeong and Kim (2002) is as follows: "Glycyrrhizin affects cellular signaling pathways such as protein kinase C; casein kinase II; and transcription factors such as activator protein 1 and nuclear factor. Furthermore, Glycyrrhizin and its aglycone metabolite upregulate expression of inducible nitrous oxide synthetase and production of nitrous oxide macrophages." Nitrous oxide inhibits replication of several viruses, such as Japanese encephalitis virus (Lin *et al.*, 1997), which can also be inhibited by glycyrrhizin.

Licorice root can act as an aid in quitting smoking. It looks just like an old cheroot cigar, and you can keep a stick of it on hand and suck on it in place of a cigarette whenever you feel like smoking; it can act as cigarette substitute. It works by helping satisfy the oral cravings that people who are addicted to cigarettes seem to have (Duke, 1997).

Toxicity:
Licorice has many side effects, such as:
> Swelling of the face and limbs;
> Body weaknesses;
> Headaches;
> Lethargy;
> Sodium and water retention;
> Excessive secretion of potassium;
> Increased blood pressure;
> Can lead to heart failure and cardiac arrest.

Licorice should not be used by pregnant women.

Chapter 23

Lavender: English
Karpuravallhi : (Malayalam)
            : (Hindi)

Introduction:
Scientific Name: *Lavandula officinalis*
Family Name: *Lamiaceae, Labiate*

Lavender is one of the most important fragrant plants in the world. Its flowers provide essential oils that have been used for several years ago in the manufacturing of perfumeries and aromas.
This plant has many species, such as *Lavandula delphinensis* and *Lavandula fragrans*.

Lavandula officinalis is grown in France and is the major lavender recognized in the French pharmacopoeia.

Lavandin, a hybrid plant bred by crossing *Lavandula hybrida* and the true lavender plant, is referred to as "bastard lavandin." Its essential oil is used mostly in the cosmetic and fragrance industry because it is less expensive than pure lavender (Clarke, 2002). Recently, synthetic products have begun to be substituted for natural oils. However, nowadays natural products are being put under the spotlight, and people are more and more going back into the usage of natural products (Pokorny, 1991).

History and folklore:
When lavender is added to ritual baths, it is expected to purify the soul as well as heal. It is whispered that carrying this herb with you enables the carrier to see ghosts. Men are sexually aroused when carrying lavender, and in addition it helps them acquire strength and courage. It was found that lavender was mentioned in more than 260,000 works of literature in the English language, citing three main purposes: first for

its nice smell when storing bed sheets and clothes; second, as a pleasant scent for the body or to get rid of unpleasant smells, and third, as a calming or restorative agent, which is closest to the current use of lavender, which is for psychological problems such as inducing sleep and for relaxation (Smith, 2003).

The word "lavender" comes from the Spanish word "lavandera," the famous plant used by laundresses for scenting linen. Indeed, the scenting of bed sheets is widely talked about in much ancient and recent literature.

This makes senses because lavender was associated with calming effects, as observed below, and/or moth repellent activity. As mentioned by Michael Kirk-Smith, "Laying up in lavender was apparently such a well-accepted and known practice so that it was able to be used metaphorically as meaning "putting away in storage" in a general sense. This could include lovers and others."

Habitat:
Lavender likes light sandy soil and full sun. It grows up to 18 inches and should be mulched in colder climates for winter protection, being a perennial. Lavendula plants are loaded with small flower heads, and grow at high altitudes on dry, limy soils. Spike lavender, however, grows at much lower attitudes, is cheaper and easier to cultivate and gives high yields of oil. It is mostly found in Spain. Lavandin grows at very low altitudes and yields twice as much oil as the true lavandin plant (Clarke, 2002).

Chemistry:
The different types of lavenders' oils contain different amounts of constituents' compounds.

Lavender (the true one and not the hybrid) is composed of Linalyl acetate (34%), Linalool (30%), Cineole (0.57%), Limonene, Lavandulol and camphor (0.21%).

The spike Lavender, however, contains Linalyl acetate (5.37%), Linalool (43%), Cineole (24%), Limonene, Lavandulol and camphor (14%).

The hybrid lavender contains Linalyl acetate (23%), Linalool (41%), Cineole (5%), Limonene, Lavandulol and camphor (3.51%) (Clarke, 2002).

In general, lavender plants are made of:
 Volatile oil: containing linalyl acetate, with linalool, lavandulyl acetate, borneol, camphor, limonene, cadinene, caryophyllene, 4-butanolide, 5-pentyl-5-pentanolide;

 Coumarins : Umbelliferone, herniarin, coumarins, dihydro-coumarin.

 Miscellaneous: Triterpenes such as ursolic acid and Flavonoids such as luteolin.

Medicinal value:
Lavender is an antidepressant and is used in combination with other herbs for fighting depression, nervous tension, headaches and stress. True lavender, due to its high ester and alcohol content, is considered a desirable aromatotherapy and has no contraindications. Spike lavender has a low ester and high camphor content; it is useful for respiratory infections, for muscular pain and as an insecticide. The hybrid lavender is considered an inferior essential oil. It is used in many therapeutic treatments and has rare contraindications (Clarke, 2002).

According to Duke (1997) Lavender oil can be used for the treatment of burns by dipping the burned part in the oil immediately, for the recovery of fainting by smelling it, for carpal tunnel syndrome by applying it, to get relief from pain, for psoriasis and for vaginitis due to Trichomonas and Gardnerella infections.

Functional properties:
This beautiful and refreshing herb has many uses: cosmetic, culinary and medicinal. It is an effective herb for headaches especially when they are related to stress. It is used as a gentle strengthening tonic for the nervous system; and may be used in states of nervous debility and exhaustion. It can also be used to soothe and promote natural sleep. Externally, lavender oil may be used as a stimulating liniment to help ease the aches and pains of rheumatism. Scientific research done on the clinical use and psychological effects of lavender have started to

take place and be a topic of interest. However, since ancient times ordinary people have been using it for many purposes, such as to influence psychological states, and in particular, for calming, relaxation and sleep-inducement (Smith, 2003).

Lavender affects two extremely important aspects of psychological well-being, which are being in a positive good mood and having an optimistic view of the future and what it may bring. Many studies have based their research on these two hypotheses of the effects of Lavender on the human being and good mood (Morris, 2002). Psychological positive mood changes were found after a bathing regimen of lavender in the water was used for 14 consecutive days. Many changes should occur, such as decreased energetic arousal, tense arousal, hedonic tone and anger frustration. It is very clear that physical illness can be a consequence of psychological illness, such as anxiety and depression. This can produce a vicious circle that relates physical well-being to psychological well-being, so in order to have one accomplished you have to be sure the other is going as well, also (Evans *et al.*, 2000).

Psychological well-being can be identified as a state in which a person has optimism and positive mood states predominating (Kahneman *et al.*, 1999). One very important aromatotherapy regimen consists of diluting an essential oil with lavender oil and adding it to a warm bath at home. This phenomena is considered relaxing, and in addition, it allows the absorption of the oil by the body's external tissue, allowing for a "gentle medication." Lavender oil is considered very effective by many studies (Lawless, 1994). In addition, general arousal was also reduced by lavender oil. Daily bathing with lavender oil is mood enhancing. It will lead to a marked reduction in the number of negative responses to the future. Adding lavender to baths may help to reduce pessimism in individuals who are not "clinically depressed."

"However lavender oil cannot replace any clinical treatment such as psychotherapy and pharmacological interventions in the treatment of severe psychological disorders, but they tend to be more useful for the treatment of psychological responses to everyday life-stresses." Separately, lavender oil showed a clear antifungal action against dermatophyte infection (Cassella, 2002).

Chapter 24

Thyme: **English**
(Malayalam)
(Hindi)

Introduction:
Scientific Name: *Thymus* sp.
Family Name: *Labiatae*

There are more than 150 species of the genus Thymus, including *Thymus vulgaris* or common-thyme, *Thymus zygis* or Spanish-thyme, *Thymus serphyllum* or wild-thyme, *Thymus mastichina* and *Thymus capitatus.*
Thyme plant is a naturalized, perennial plant. Its leaves are small, opposite and entire. Its flowers are purple or sometimes white and accumulate in dense terminal clusters blossoming in July (Cecil, 1998). There are two different species of thymus (family Lamiaceae) that are used: the first one is garden or common thyme *T. vulgaris L.,* the second is Spanish thyme, known as *T. zygis. L.* However, the common thyme contains the higher amount of volatile oil (3.4 vs. 1.38 percent) (Duke, 1999). Thyme has been known since long ago for its aromatic properties.

Religious importance and folklore:
It is believed that Thyme is burnt to purge and disinfect magical rooms and spaces, as well as to bring good health.

The earliest recorded use of thyme was 3000 BC in Sumeria. The Sumerians used it as an antiseptic. Mummifications was an excellent way to preserve a dead body, and still to day, people have questions about this; however it was found that Egyptians did use thyme plants in this process.

Thyme was a very popular herb during the days of the ancient Greeks and Romans. Greeks used it for massage and in bath oils, as incense, and for medicinal purposes. They believed that when a person has a smell similar to thyme, he will have a flattering odor. Before going into a battle, Egyptians would bathe in thyme baths. Thyme was also considered the source of the tastiest honey in ancient Athens, and nowadays, people tend to indirectly feed their bees with thyme so that they will produce sweeter and more nutrient condensed honey.

Habitat:

This perennial plant prefers warm, sunny fields and can reach up to 15 inches. It is found in dry, open areas of northern New Jersey. It can also found in a wild state in plains and hills just like other wild plants such as lavender, and rosemary. *Thymus vulgaris* can grow in specific Mediterranean areas such as France, Spain, Algeria and Morocco.

Chemistry:

The basic constituents of thyme are mostly oils. This oil is composed of many phenols like thymol (30.7-70.9 percent), Borneol, Geraniol, Geranyl acetate, 1,8-Cineole, Terpinolene, linalool and carvacrol (2.5-14.6 percent) (Clarke, 2002). Flavonols, tannins and triterpenes are also constituents of this plant (Duke, 1999).

Thyme contains essential oils and polymers such as cellulose (mixture of hemicellulose and cellulose) and lignin. Chemical analysis shows the content of thyme as water, ash, essential oils, extractive substances and holocellulose.

These contents vary according to the four seasons of the year. Many analyses have shown that the cellulose level was higher than the lignin level in wet periods during the growth of the plant, and the opposite was found in dry periods. The total ash and essential oil levels were found to be high during the period of heavy rain (Kaloustian *et al.*, 2003).

The presence of lignin and holocellulose can increase the risk of fire, due to the presence of essential oils, (Leoni *et al.*, 2001) flammable volatile substances present in cellulose, and numerous oxygenated compounds such as alcohol, carbonyl and carboxylic acids (Masson and Deglise, 1982).

Main use:

Thyme oil is used mainly for flavoring food items. It is also used in the cosmetic industry for soap and perfumes. The thyme oils with high phenol content are used in phyto-pharmaceutical products and have been used as additives for pet foods, due to their antibiotic properties (Hartwig *et al.*, 2003).

Thyme has been used for centuries in cooking. Thyme is added to many sauces: pizza sauce, spaghetti sauce, lasagna and many other dressings. It is one of the most important breakfast items in Asian countries, where it is prepared as a "mankoushe." Thyme is also added to many bakery items, such as cakes, kaak and fatayer. Along with sesame and olive oil, thyme adds to the taste of a sandwich. Finally, thyme can add a desirable taste to many dishes, such as stew, soups and more.

Medicinal and functional Properties:
This herb is a powerful antiseptic used for many reasons, such as fighting anemia, bronchial ailments, intestinal disturbances, against tooth decay, fungal infections such as athlete's foot and skin parasites such as scabies and lice. It is good for indigestion, flatulence and a cold. Its oil is very useful as an expectorant and as an antiseptic, and thyme's oil was found to function in relieving bronchospasm, as well (Reiter and Brandt, 1985).

The spasmolytic effect of the plant will be enhanced due to the flavonoid content. The thymol component, which is present in large amount in thyme plants, acts an antiseptic and stomach-soothing compound that prevents blood clotting, and therefore protects the heart from sudden attacks and strokes (Duke, 1997). According to Duke (1997), Thyme contains anti-aging chemicals that can be used by soaking in hot baths, and this also helps back muscle spasms.

It is usually consumed as a tea, prepared by boiling 1 to 2 grams of the plant per cup of water. One cup of tea can be had two to three times a day.

It can be sweetened with either sugar or honey, which will enhance its efficacy and accentuate its taste (Duke, 2001). In a different manner, if we use dry thyme tea (1 teaspoon), it may ease aching muscles in the neck, shoulders and back, therefore relieving tension and headaches.

Used externally, thyme might be a helpful anti-aging product by adding it to hot baths. Its aromatic oil helps remove stress, as well. In addition, thyme can be used as a deodorant, as it has an antibacterial action against the microorganism that leads to unpleasant apocrine secretion, which will leads to a body's bad smell (Duke, 1997).

Thyme's essential oil is responsible for the inhibition of *Aspergillus parasitius* growth and its aflatoxin (Iraj and Abyaneh, 2004). The *Aspergillus* species produce a highly toxic and carcinogenic metabolite named Aflatoxin B1 (Allameh *et al.*, 2001). The aflatoxin deactivation process is characterized by the fact that it destroys the mycelia and spores of the toxic fungi, which may proliferate under favorable conditions This inhibition in mycelial growth, which is dependent on the type of the essential oil present in thyme, was observed to be associated with significantly decreased levels of aflatoxin production (Iraj and Abyaneh, 2004).

Thyme oils shows high antimicrobial effects compared to the oils of the other plants (Juliano *et al.*, 2000).These antimicrobial properties are related to the chemical composition of the oils, which depend upon the different species of the genus *Thymus* (Granger and Passet,1973). Essential oils present in this plant have exhibited the ability to inhibit microbial as well as fungal growth and destroy microorganisms. *Thymus broussonettii* exhibited the greatest potency of most of the microorganisms.

Part B. Additional Chapters

Chapter 25   **A. Ajowan B. Caraway seed**
Chapter 26   **Basil**
Chapter 27   **Chamomile**
Chapter 28   **Coriander**
Chapter 29   **Fennel**
Chapter 30   **Fenugreek**
Chapter 31   **Mint**
Chapter 32   **Mustard**

Chapter 25

A. *Ajowan:* English
Ayamodakam:(Malayalam)
Ajwan:(Hindi)

Introduction:
Scientific Name:*Carum ajowan*
Family Name: *Umbelliferae*

Ajawan is also known as Bishop's Weed. Not used by many countries, Ajowan was first cultivated in sothern India. It is now widespread in Egypt, Iran and Pakistan.

Habitat:
The plant belongs to the *Umbelleferae* family, and it looks like a caraway seed plant with flowers and seeds. The seeds are used as spices, and have a strong pungent flavor like Anise seed.

Religious and folk importance:
The boiled water of the seed is used to treat colic in children from the time of birth in south India.

Main uses :
It is used in Indian cookery by adding it to lentil dishes with oregano and black pepper. It is also used in vegetables, meat dishes, beans, pulses, pakoras, biscuits and Indian breads, as well as eaten raw or with sugar after a meal to prevent gas and to sweeten breath.

Medicinal value and functional properties:
The seed contains thymol oil, which has a slightly hot taste.

It is good for babies with colic. Also, it can be used as a mouth wash (Ellen, 1997).

B. *Caraway seed:* English
   Karimjirakam : *Malayalam*
   Shia-jira :*Hindi*

Introduction:
Scintific Name: *Carum carvi*
Family Name: *Umbelliferae*

Caraway seeds have been used since the Stone Age onwards; it is an ancient spice.

Religious and folklore:
Egyptians, as early as 2500 BC, put this spice with their dead to keep away bad spirits. In the USA this spice was given to children in church to stop restless movement, hence the nickname, "meetin" seed.

Folklore had it that caraway prevented fickleness and was as a common ingredient of love potions.

Habitat:
The caraway plant grows 2 ft in height and is a biennial with fine feathery leaves and white-to-pink flowers. It produces capsules containing the seeds, and when ripe they explode and release the seeds. The seeds are long and thin and dark in color compared to Aniseed. The plant once grew in the wild in Europe and western Asia, but now it is cultivated there.

Chemical nature:
Carum Caravi contains 3-7% essential oil with odoriferous component (S)-(+)-carvone65%; (R)-(+)-limonene about 50% and other terpenes namely α - and β-pinene, sabinene, car-3-ene, isomers of dihydrocarvone, dihydrocarveol, and carveol. It also contains 10-18%

fixed oil, ca.20%, protein, ca.20% carbohydrate and flavonoids (Bisset, 2001).

Main use:
Caraway seeds are used to decorate cakes, bread, and biscuits. It is also used in the preparation of vegetables, soups, and meat, and also in the preparation of "Biryani rice" by Indians. The essential oil in the seeds gives the flavor to confectionery, gin and rice.

Medicinal and functional properties.
Caraway seeds can be eaten raw to prevent gas after meals, aid in digestion and sweeten the breath, as ajowan seeds. Caraway seeds, after boiling, can be given to babies to relieve colic. It promotes milk secretion in nursing mothers. It is used in perfumes, after shave lotions and soaps in India. It is used for ear infections. It has an aphrodisiac effect, and ladies can rub the seeds and powder into their skin to get a better complexion (Ellen, 1997).

Chapter 26

Basil: English
Rama Thulasi: (Malayalalam)
Babul, Babuyi tulsi: (Hindi)

Introduction:
Scientific Name: *Ocimum basilicum*
Family Name: *Lamiaceae*

Basil was first cultivated in the Mediterranean region, but is now cultivated in France, Morocco, Italy, Egypt, Bulgaria, Hungry and India.

There are over forty varieties of basil. Sweet or common basil is the main culinary variety and has the finer flavor, followed closely by the larger lettuce-leaf basil.

The flavors of the other popular types, the purple-leaved variety and the low-growing bush (also known as dwarf basil), are inferior and grown more for ornamental purposes. Other kinds of basil that can be used in the kitchen include curly or Italian basil and lemon basil. Wild or hedge basil is, in fact, not basil at all.

Chemical Composition:
The essential oil content of basil varies from 0.04 to 0.70% depending on the variety, origin and when collected. The oil consists mainly of linalool (in some up to75% of the oil) methylchavicol (oestragole up to 87%) and eugenol (up to 20%). It also contains monoterpene (namely ocimine and cineole) as well as sequiterpene and phenylpropanes. In addition, it contains tannins, flavinoids, caffeic acid and aesculodes and saponins (Bisset, 2001).

Religious importance:
It is believed that basil is a protection against evil and negativity and

helps in attracting and keeping love. The *Ocimum scantum* variety in India is considered sacred and called Krishna Thulasi and is used in Temple for "Puja." *Ocimum bascilicum* is called Rama Thulasi in Kerala, India, and is used for cooking.

Basil is also used in rituals to bring prosperity. Basil placed in someone's pocket is believed to bring fortune and wealth. A married man, if wondering about any possible infidelity from his spouse, can stay calm, since it was believed that if you sprinkled some basil leaves on your wife during sleep, it will drive infidelities away. Basil is also known as Sweet Basil. It is an annual herb which is cultivated mostly in India and Iran. In India, it was considered to be a sacred herb. For this reason, it was a great honor to the dead to be buried with leaves of basil, because, it would give them direct passport to heaven, as well.

The botanical name of Basil is derived from the Greek "to be fragrant." Notwithstanding, Greeks never liked basil and believed that scorpions lived under pots of basil. In Ancient Rome, the name for basil was Basilescus, which referred to the fire breathing dragon Basilik; they thought that ingesting Basil would protect them against Basilik. In Italy, basil is considered a sign of love. Well drained, rich soil and complete sun are essentials for the growth of basil. Some areas of North America have the perfect climate for this annual, which reaches a height of 2-3 feet (Duke, 1997).

Main use:
Fresh basil has a slightly sweet flavor with a bite. It has a gorgeous fragrance. It is one herb that cannot be dried successfully, because of intense flavor loss. It can, however, be blanched and immediately frozen, when freshly picked from the garden in large quantities. Basil may also be preserved in olive oil, lending a beautiful bouquet and flavor to the oil. It is also popular for making herbed vinegars. Both herbed oils and vinegars make attractive and useful additions to kitchen counters and make wonderful gifts. Basil is considered a wonderful herb for egg dishes. It is excellent with beef and fish, eggplant and zucchini. It has a particular affinity with tomatoes, adding an exquisite depth of flavor.

One can prepare an easy and delightful meal simply with pasta, tomatoes, and basil. The flavor of basil is put to its full use in simple tomato salads and tomato-based sauces such as pasta sauces and pizza sauces. Basil is a valued part of the cuisines of Italy, North Africa, the Middle East, southern France, and Spain. Tearing basil is preferred to chopping, and be sure to add a chiffonade of fresh basil on top of the dish you are serving; the flavor of the dish will be more pronounced. Adding basil to hot dishes at the end of cooking will also give them a more intense flavor. The plant is also used for the preservation of fish (Bisset, 2001).

Medicinal value:

Basil is the best plant used for the treatment of many upsetting stomach cramps, vomiting, fevers, colds, flu, headaches, whooping cough, and menstrual pains. Furthermore, it reduces stomach acid and contributes to the treatment of ulcers. To extract the poison of an insect bite from the body, the herb should be used externally only. It is known for eliminating worms from the intestines, and when applied in oil form, to treat skin acne (Duke, 2001). In addition, Basil can be used as an anthelmintic, cardiotonic, expectorant, diuretic insecticidal antibacterial, rheumatoid arthritis, flatulence, opthalmia, giddiness, leucoderma, ringworm, pruritus, asthma and for malarial fevers. The seeds are effective as an aphrodisiac, stimulant, diuretic, for burning sensations, wounds, hemorrhages, hemorrhoids, seminal weakness, chronic dysentery and general debility (Warrier *et al.*, 1995).

Chapter 27

Chamomile: **English**
:*(Malayalam)*
:*(Hindi)*

Introduction:
Scientific Name: *Matricaria chamomilla* **(German chamomile),** *Anthemus nobilis* **(Roman chamomile)** and *Anthemis mixta* **(Moroccan).**
Family Name: *Asteraceae (Compositae)*

Chamomile is a 6 inches to 2-foot tall naturalized annual found in waste areas and along roadsides.
It can be very confused when hearing the word "chamomile," because there are several types of it. The most expensive one is the German. Chamomile leaves are alternate, finely-divided and described as pineapple-or apple-scented. It has a pleasant aromatic odor and an aromatic bitter taste. The stem is smooth; flowers are white and daisy like, and they blossom in May (Cecil, 1998).

Religious importance:
It is believed that chamomile attracts money and if added to incense produces a relaxed state for better meditation. When added to ritual baths, it can help in love matters by attracting a wanted lover and in bringing couples together.

Habitat:
Chamomile is an annual that adapts to almost all kind of soils, it likes water and full sun. It is cultivated mainly in Europe and western Asia, and naturalized in the USA.

Chemistry:
Chamomile is made of essential oil, apigenins, bisabolene, alpha-

bisabolol, borneol, farnesol, furfural, matricarin, chamazulene and chlorogenic acid (D'Amelio, 1999).

The typical compositions of the three species are as follows:

Roman: esters of angelic and tiglic acids, pinene, farnesol, nerodiol, pinacarvone, cineole;

German: chamazulene, farnesene, bisabobol, bisabobol oxide, cis-spiro ether;

Moroccan: santolina alcohol, germacene, trans-spirocarveol.

Chamomile oil is extracted from both the flowers and stalk of the species *Chamomilla recuttia*. This oil has a deep blue color with a characteristic odor and bitter, aromatic taste. This blue color is due to the presence of chamazulene, which is produced from matricine during chamomile distillation.

Today, the most wanted chamomile oils are the ones which are rich in the α- bisabolo component, because it is very effective in the antiphlogogenic properties. Chamomile chemotypes differ according to the composition of its essential oils (Schilcher, 1973). Depending on the geographic location, chamomile species may differ in the natural occurrence of these chemotypes.

Main uses:

Chamomile is used in many dishes, especially bread, kaak, pastries and cakes. It can be boiled in water and used as a tea drink. When used as tea, sugar should be added because if not it may cause hypotension.

Medicinal value

Chamomile herb is used as tea for nerves and menstrual cramps. The tea is also useful for babies and small children with colds and stomach troubles. For inducing sleep in insomniac conditions and to wash sore eyes and open sores, this herb is advised.

It is an:

Anti-inflammatory;
Carminative;
Healing tonic;
Analgesic;
Calmative;
Antispasmodic;
Relaxing;
Mentally soothing (Clarke, 2002).

In addition, according to Satyavati *et al.*, (1987) it can be used as an expectorant, anthelmentic, diuretic and for the ailments of children for dentition trouble, stomach disorders, ear ache, pains and convulsions, flatulence, hysteria , intermittent fevers and antiseptic. It can be used as an emetic with warm water and strong preparation. Weak infusion acts as a mild tonic and febrifuge. It can be used for rheumatism, neuralgia and hemorrhoids .

If boiled, one can use its steam for facial applications such as cleaning facial pores from impurities and reducing puffiness. And don't forget that by boiling chamomile flowers and adding it to light hair, it can add highlights.

Chamomile is added to many tropical oils that are used to relieve pain and aches (D'Amelio, 1999). The syrup of fresh or dried flowers with white wine can be used for jaundice, dropsy, nervousness and uterine problems (Cecil, 1998).

Chapter 28

Coriander: **English**
Kottamalli: (Malayalam)
Dhaniya :(Hindi)

Introduction:

Scientific Name: *Coriandrum sativum*
Family Name: *Apiaceae*

Since ancient time coriander has been used as a spice, both leaves and seeds. Egyptians used coriander as an aphrodisiac while Greeks used it to flavor wines. In early Egyptian, Greek and Sanskrit texts, it was written about coriander as a spice. The name coriander came from the Greek "koris," meaning "bug," as the unripe coriander seeds have an unpleasant odor, as that of a "green beetle." But the ripe seeds have a good aroma. Since it has a narcotic effect it is nicknamed "dizzycorn" (Ellen, 1997).

Habitat:
Earlier coriander was grown in southern Europe, the Mediterranean region and the Near East. Now it has been grown throughout the world, especially Morocco, the former USSR, Romania, Bulgaria and Turkey. It is an annual plant of 2 feet height with flowers of pink-mauve color. The seeds are bright green and round-to-oval in shape, and become beige when ripe. The seeds are used mainly as spices. The leaves have a pungent odor, resemble parsley and are used as herbs and to flavor many food preparations.

Chemical Nature:
The main constituents are 1% essential oil, 60-70% D-(+)-linalool, 20% monoterpene hydrocarbons, camphor, geraniol and geranyl acetate. The bed bug smell of the unripe fruit and herb is due to trans-

Triec-2-en-1-al.

Main use:
In India, the seeds are roasted and kept or used to make curry powder, which can be used for meat preparations and vegetable preparations like "Sambar," beans *etc.*, and can be sprinkled on savory dishes, and fish *etc.* The powder is used in many preparations of vegetables, meat and at times for fish. Coriander leaves are used to garnish soups and also for the curry preparation of both vegetables and meat in Eastern and Mediterranean cooking. Coriander leaves are also used for special South Indian preparations like "Uppuma," "Sambar," "Byriani rice" *etc.*

Medicinal and functional properties:
Coriander seeds aid digestion and reduce flatulence. The essential oil of the coriander seeds are used for tooth paste and in perfumes. It is used in massage oil and also used to treat facial neuralgia and cramps. The seeds are used as anthelmintic, stomachic, carminative, antipyretic diuretic, expectorant and bronchitis. The seeds are also used for burning sensations, vomiting, flatulence, diarrhea, dysentery, and hemorrhoids. The leaves of coriander are used as an astringent, anti-inflammatory, epistaxis and for chronic conjunctivitis, and the paste of leaves is used for allergic inflammation (Warrier *et al.*, 1994).

Chapter 29

Fennel : *English*
Perumjirakam : (Malayalam)
Saumph: (Hindi)

Introduction:
Scientific Name: *Foeniculum vulgare*
Family Name: *Apiaceae (Umbelleferae)*

Habitat :
The fennel plant originated in Mediterranean countries and they consider it a sacred herb that can keep away evil. For Indians, fennel forms a "love medicine" and is considered as "holy and partaking the essence of nectar"(Ellen, 1997). Since fennel grew wild around the village of Marathon, the ancient Greeks called fennel marathon. Fennel is now grown throughout the world, namely in Egypt, India, the Far East, Germany, Italy, France, parts of Africa, China, Bulgaria, Hungry and Romania. In America, fennel was brought by the American colonists to north America and now it grows wild through out the USA. The plant grows up to 6 1/2 ft. tall with feathery leaves, bearing umbels of yellow flowers with oblong, ellipsoidal, slightly-curved yellowish-brown seeds.

Main use:
The seeds are used mainly in the preparation of meat, vegetables and poached eggs. The bulb and root are used in fresh salads, as they have a good flavor. The leaves can be used fresh in curry. Italians use fennel in roasted pork. The fennel oil is also used in pickles.

Chemical composition:
According to Bisset (2001) fennel seeds contain 2-6% essential oils consisting of 50-70% sweetish *trans*-anethole and 20% bitter and camphoraceous (+)-fenchone. They also contain methylchavicol, anisaldehyde and some terpanoid hydrocarbons, namely α-pinene,

α-phellandrene and limonene. The fruit of fennel contains fixed oil, protein, organic acid and flavonoids. Fennel also contains the following chemicals namely calcium, magnesium, phosphorous, sodium, folic acids, vitamin c, potassium and phyto- oestrogens.

Medicinal value and functional properties:
By eating fennel, weight can be reduced and strength increased. Fennel seeds are used to treat wheezing and shortness of breath. In olden times in India and China, fennel was used for scorpion and snake bite poisoning (Ellen, 1997). The leaves are used to sharpen the memory. The seeds are also used as an expectorant, haematinic, anthelmintic cardiac stimulant, diuretic carminative, aphrodisiac, for treating hemorrhoids, fever, skin disease and inflammations (Warrier *et al.*, 1995). It relieves hiccups when taken with one or two drops of sugar. It can relieve abdominal cramps by taking the essential oil mixed with honey in a cup of warm water. It also helps women during menopause and start menstruation for girls. The oil used in creams or body lotions can enlarge breasts and prevent breast from sagging. It is also used in lotions to moisturize the body. It can aid in prostrate cancer treatment for men, as well. In folk medicine it is used as a galactagogue for lactating women to increase their milk. It is used as a decoction for eye lotion and for visual disorders. To enhance different tastes fennel is also used in different food preparations. It is given to infants and small children to dissolve the mucous of the respiratory tract. It can be used for flatulence and cramps, such as pain in the gastrointestinal tract. Hence in hotels in north India, after dinner they provide fennel mixed with Ajowan and some sweets to munch on, which also removes bad breath from the mouth. Fleas on dogs will be prevented if we put it in their food.

Contra indications:
For infants and young children, pure fennel oil must not be used as it can produce laryngeal spasms, dyspnoea and excitatory states. Wild fennel can be confused with poison helmock and should never be used. Pregnant women should not use the essential oil of fennel. It also should not be used by those who have a blood clotting history or oestrogen-dependent breast tumors. Fennel can induce dermatitis by handling in some people.

Chapter 30

Fenugreek : *English*
Uluva: (Malayalam)
Methi: (Hindi)

Introduction:
Scientific Name : *Trigonella foenum-graecum*
Family Name: *Leguminaceae*

This spice is cultivated in east Mediterranean countries and in Greece
is used for cattle fodder and named as "Greek hay" (Ellen,1997).
It is also cultivated in India, and used as spices as well as the
leaves being used as a vegetable.

Habitat :
Fenugreek is a short, upright plant of 30-60cm height with pinnate,
oval leaves that grow in threes, produce yellow white flowers, and
the seeds are produced in 5-7.5cm pods. The seeds are three sided,
greenish-brown, and with a deep groove across one corner. The plant
and seeds have a sweet aroma with a bitter taste.

Religious and folk importance:
The seeds and sprouts are used for old flock for breast enlargement
and for problems with menstrual pain to postmenopausal vaginal
dryness in women.

Chemical structure:
Fenugreek seeds contain diosgenin, a chemical compound. This
compound is used to produce semi synthetic forms of the female sex
hormone estrogen. The leaf of fenugreek contains choline which can
prevent Alzheimer's disease. It also contains beta carotene, which also
prevents or slows down Alzheimer's (Dukes, 1997).

Main use:
In Africa and India the seeds are roasted and added to chutneys and
curries for flavor. The roasted seeds are soaked and eaten like beans

by Africans. Egyptians and Ethiopians add it to bread. Sprouted seeds are a good source of phytoestrogen and are used in salads. It is good for the sharpness of memory.

Medicinal value and functional properties:

The ingredients of fenugreek are used in modern medicine. It reduces blood cholesterol and sugar. It is used as a gargle for sore throat. It is used as an antipyretic and hence reduces fever. It is used to heal wounds (Ellen,1997). Because of its phytoestrogen, a paste made of the seeds is used for breast enlargement for women who have small breasts. It is used as a galatagouge to increase milk supply for newborns from biblical times onward. In addition to the sex hormone estrogen, another compound is present in fenugreek which has been shown to increase milk flow, and in Middle Eastern countries it is given to women for that. Fenugreek seeds contain mucilage, which helps to prevent constipation and also to treat diarrhea. It works as an aphrodisiac in women because of the estrogen content (Duke, 1997). In addition to the above usage in medicine the aqueous extract works as an antibacterial. In smallpox, the infusion of the seeds are used to produce a cooling effect. For burns, poultice of the leaves is used. The seeds are used for vomiting, anorexia, cough, bronchitis and colonitis, and also as an emollient, carminative and astringent. The powder of the seeds and leaves is used in veterinary medicine (Warrier *et al.*,1996).

Chapter 31

Mint: *English*

Pudina : (Hindi)
Putina : (Malayalam)

Introduction:
Scientific Name: *Menthae piperitae folium (Peppermint leaf), Mentha arvensis (Japanese mint), M. arvensis var piperascensm, M. spicata, M. citrata, M .cardica, M. longifolia.*
Family Name: *Lamiaceae (Labiatae)*

There are many species and hybrids of Mentha, are available in different countries depending on the chemistry of the mint oil, menthol and various constituents.

The mint plant is a 10-60 cm high aromatic herb with a creeping rhizome, and grows all over the world. Leaves are simple, oblong, and ovate with serrate margins, shortly petioled and placed on opposite sides of the stem. Flowers are whitish and slightly lilac in color, with a strong characteristic and very aromatic odor.

Part used: Both the leaves and whole plant are used.

Historical perspective: Mint is cultivated in Bulgaria, Greece, Spain and India, and now in Germany, northern Europe and the USA, as well.

Chemical composition:
The plant contains mainly mint oil, menthol and various other chemicals. The percentage of composition varies depending on the place grown. According to Malla *et al.*, (1962), *M. arvensis* contains natural oil with methanol of 70-80%. The methanol consists of 40-50% methanol and (50-60%) dementholized oil. The dementholised oil consists of menthol 41.7%. (borate ester). The redementhaolised oil is made up of methylacetate, α-β-hexenyl acetate dl-methionene, dl-

isomenthene and carvomenthone in the company of carbonyls and limonine, α-pinene, α- thujene and santene included in hydrocarbons. Arora and Singh (1968) reported a number of amino acids, namely Aspartic acid, glutamic acid, serine, glycene, threonine, alanine, asparagine, valine, leucine, isoleucine, phenylalanine, methionine and lysine from the ethanolic extract of *M. arvensis* leaves. Menthofuran, always present in *M. piperitae* whatever its origin, could be absent or detected in traces in *M. arvensis*. Otherwise, both appear similarly and are difficult to differentiate by appearance (Bisset, 2001). Baslas (1983) reviewed the phytochemical studies of 26 Mentha species.

Main use:
Mint, due to its great aroma, is used in the cooking of meats and vegetables throughout the world. It is used in Biryani rice in India. Due to its antiseptic action it is also used in mouth washes and in coffee and tea to relieve throat pain. In addition, *M. piperitae* is used in tooth paste, and used in toffee to get rid of bad breath. It is used in ice creams, chocolates and sweets.

Medicinal and functional properties:
The leaves are used as an antiseptic, anthelmintic, diuretic, antiemetic, carminative, stomachic, and expectorant. The leaves can also be used for contraception, flatulence, colic, cardiac debility, skin disease, jaundice (by increasing the production of bile), fever, amenorrhea, dental caries, asthma, peptic ulcer, cough and bronchitis (Bisset, 2001, Warrier *et al.*, 1996). Nayak and Dutta (1961) reported the vibriocidal activity against *V. cholerae* of menthol. The ethanolic extract of plants showed antibacterial, antifungal, antiprotozoal or antiviral activities (Satyavati *et al.*, 1987).

Chapter 32

Mustard: English
Katuku: (Malayalam)
Rayi: (Hindi)

Scientific Name:
There are four kinds of mustard;1) *Brassica juncea* - Indian Mustard;
2) *Brassica nigra* –Karinkatuku; 3) *Brassica alba-* White mustard and
4) *Brassica campestris* -Brown mustard.
Family Name: *Brassicaceae* of the *cruceferae* family.

Originally native in the Mediterranean region, it has spread to
Romania, the USSR, Turkey, Canada, China, India, Nepal and
Pakistan. Different countries use different kinds of mustard. Japanese
use brown mustard, Indians use black mustard, English use white and
brown seeds and Americans use yellow mustard (Ellen, 1997). The
plant is an annual with a few bristles at the base and grows to a height
of 4-6 ft with long, undivided oblong leaves at the base, oblong middle
leaves and linear upper leaves with four yellow petal flowers.

Habitat:
The plant grows well in temperate zones and is cultivated throughout
India. It was introduced in Europe by early Arab traders. Mustard
seeds are very tiny and when they dry on the plant, if the plant is
shaken the seeds will fall off. So it should be harvested before the pods
containing the seeds are dried.

Religious importance and flock medicine:
Mustard seeds were found in the tomb of DIVA Akbu'n-neg in ancient
Egypt in 1786 BC. The Chinese used to burn dried mustard seeds to
produce toxic smoke (mustard gas) to drive away their enemies in the
5th century. Hot mustard baths have been used to arouse women's
libido (Ellen, 1997).

Part used:
Seed, oil and flower.

Chemical structure:

Contains 30% fixed oil (mustard oil glycosides. It further contains 1% sinapin (ester of choline with sinapic acid) and 20% mucilage (Bisset, 2001).

Main use in food processing:

Mustard seeds have a sweet taste and a pungent smell. The seeds are fried (or popped in hot oil) with onion and curry leaves and are used in preparing pickles. In Indian cuisine it is poured over some dishes before serving to get a good flavor.

Medicinal and functional properties:

Mustard seeds are acrid, bitter, thermogenic, anti-inflammatory, carminative, and anthelmintic. They are used for the treatment of Dengue fever, abdominal colic, intestinal worms, flatulence, skin disease, splenomegaly and vomiting. Large doses are used as an emetic in the case of poisoning (Warrier *et al.*, 1994). Mustard plasters, or poultice, were used to stimulate blood circulation on an area by applying it to the painful area for 10-12 minutes. It increases blood circulation in that area, becomes red and should not be kept longer as it will produce a blister. Romans use mustard in massage oil to ease stiff muscles. It is used for asthma by mixing with garlic in white wine, keeping a few days and then drinking. Mustard and honey were used for coughs as early as 1653 by Nicholas Culpeper. A pinch of mustard in cold water can relieve hiccups. Dried mustard powder mixed with honey into little balls will give a good voice to singers if eaten 2- 3 times every morning (Ellen, 1997).

Summary:

This book describes 35 herbs and spices and is divided into part A and part B. Each chapter describes different spices, and consists of family name, genus name, where it is cultivated, where is the traditional home, what type of soil the plant needed for cultivation *etc.*

In the next topic, its chemical nature, nutritional value, use of the spice in food, the medicinal value and traditional properties are described. The toxic effect if any are also described concerning the particular spices or herbs. Thus, it is a very useful book for nutritionist, for hotel managers, college teachers, microbiologists, immunologists, botanists, drug manufactures, hospital nutritionist and for physicians, both ayurvedic and allopathic doctors. This is also useful for homemakers who love to cook, to understand the use of each spice and herb and the useful action in food that they use in cooking.

The 26 spices described in part A are: Aniseed, Bay leaf, Black pepper, Capsicum, Cardamom, Cinnamon, Clove, Cumin, Curry leaf, Dill, Garlic, Ginger, Kokam and Cambodge, Nutmeg and Mace, Marjoram and Oregano, Onion, Rosemary and Sage, Saffron, Tamarind, Turmeric, Licorice, Lavender and Thyme.

In Part B, the following 9 spices are described namely, Ajowan, and Caraway seed, Basil, Chamomile, Coriander, Fennel, Fenugreek, Mint and Mustard.

References:

Adetumbi, M.A. and Lau, B.H.S. (1983). Allium sativum (garlic)- A Natural Antibiotic. *Medical Hypotheses.* **12**: 227-237.

Afifi, F. U., Khalil., E. Tamimi, S. O. and Disi, A. (1997). *J Ethnopharmacol.* **58**: 9.

Alberti, K. G. and Zimmet, P. Z. (1998). Definition, diagnosis and classification of diabetes mellitus and its complications. I. Diagnosis and classification of diabetes mellitus: provisional report of a WHO consultation. *Diabete Med.* **15** : 539-553.

Allameh, A., Razzaghiabyaneh, M., Shams, M., Rezaee,M.B.and Jaimand, K. (2001). Effect of neem leaf extract on production of Aflatoxin and fatty acid synthetase, citrate dehydrogenase and glutathione S-transferase in A. *Parasiticus Mycopathologia.* **154**: 79-84.

Al-Yahya, M. A., Rafatullah, S., Mossa, J. S., *et al.,* (1989). Gastroprotective activity of Ginger in albino Rats. *American Journal of Chinese Medicine.***17**: 51- 56.

Anon. (1956). Wealth of India., *Council of Scientific and Industrial research, New Delhi, Vol. IV* pp. 99-100.

Antoine, B. K. (1998). *Herbs as natural pharmacy.* pp. 100-125.

Arora, S. K. and Sing, M. (1968).Free amino acids of *Mentha avensis. Linn.Sci.Cult.***34**: 373.

Asha, S.K., Anila, L. and. Vijayalakshmi, N.R. (2001). Flavinoids from *Garcinia cambogia* lower lipid levels in hypercholesterolemic rats. *Food Chemistry.* **72**: 289-294.

Atal, C.K., Zutshi, U. and Rao, P.G., (1981). Scientific Evidence on the Role of Ayurvedic Herbals on the Bioavailability of Drugs. *Journal of Ethnopharmacology.* **4**: 229-232.

Baslas, R. K. (1983 a and b). Phytochemical studies of the spices of Mentha genera Part I and II *HerbaHung.* **22**: 87 and 97.

Banerjee, P., Mitra, S. R., Nandi, M., *et al.,* (1976). A preliminary report on clinical trial of Rumalaya on frozen shoulders. *Indian Med J.* **70**: 29.

Bhakuni, D. S., Dhar, M. L., Dhar, M. M., Dhawan, B. N. and Mehrotra, B.N. (1969). Screening of Indian Plants for biological activity part II *Indian J Exp. Biol.* 7: 250.

Bhattacharya, P. and Chakraborty, A. (1984) Mukanol, a probable biogenetic intermediate of pyranocarbozole alkaloids from *Murraya koeiginii Phytochemistry*.23: 471.

Belman, S. (1983). Onion and Garlic Oils and Tumor Promotion *Carcinogenesis.* 4: 1063-1065.

Beratz , A. and Cazenave, J. (1988). The effect of Flavinoids on blood vessel wall interactions. In Plant Flavonoids in Biology and medicine II: Biochemical, cellular and medicinal properties, Middleton, C.V., Harbone, J.B. and Beretz, A.(Eds)Alan R Liss New York pp. 187-200.

Bisset, N.G. (2001). Herbal drugs and Phytopharmaceuticals. Medpharm scientific publishers CRC press UK and USA.pp.45- 537.

Bisset, N. G. and Wichtl, M. (2000). Liquiritiae radix. *Herbal drugs and phytopharmaceuticals (English language edition)* pp. 301-304.

Block, E. (1985). The chemistry of garlic and onions. *Scientific American.* 252: 94-97.

Bone, M. E., Wilkinson, D. J. Young, J. R., *et al.,* (1990) Ginger in Postoperative Nausea and Vomiting. *Anaesthesia.* 45: 669-671.

Bordia, A. (1978). Effects of garlic on human platelet aggregation *in vitro. Atherosclerosis* 30: 355-360.

Bordia, A., Bansal, H.C., Arora, S. K. and Singh, S.V. (1975). Effects of the Essential oils of Garlic and Onions on alimentary hyperlipidemia. *Atheroscerosis.* 21:15-19.

Boullin, D. J. (1981). Garlic as a platelet Inhibitor". *Lancet* 1: 779-777.

Boxer, M., Roberts, M., Grammer, L. (1997). Cumin Anaphylaxis, a case report. *J. Allergy and Clinical Immunology*.99: 722-723.

Kelly, B. D., Gavin, B.E., Clarke, M., Lane, A. and Larkin, C. (2003). Nutmeg and Psychosis. *Schizophrenia Research.* 60 : 95-96.

Brenner, N., Frank, O.S. and Knight, E. (1993). Chronic nutmeg psychosis.

J. R. Soc. Med **86:** 179-180.

Brodnitz, M. H., Pascale, J.V. and Derslice, L.V (1971.a). Flavor components of garlic extracts. *Journal of Agricultural food chemistry.* **19:** 273-377.

Burnham, B. E. (1995). Garlic as a possible risk for postoperative bleeding. *Plast Reconstr Surg.* **95:** 213.

Cai, L. and Wu, C. D. (1996). Compounds from clove possessing growth inhibitory activity against oral pathogens *Journal of Natural Products.* **59:** 987-990.

Caporaso, N., Smah, S. M. and Eng, R. H. K. (1983). Antifungal Activity in Human Urine and Serum after Ingestion of Garlic". *Antimicrobial Agents and Chemotherapy* **23:** 700-702.

Castleman, M. (1989) What should you do? *Medical Self-Care magazine* **52:** 11-12.

Cassella, S. (2002). Synergistic Antifungal activity of tea tree and Lavender essential oils against dermatophyte infection. *International Journal of Aromatotherapy* **12:** 2-15.

Catapano, A. L. (1997). Antioxidant effect of Flavonoids. *Angiology.* **48:** 39-44.

Cecil, C. S. (1998). *Botany and healing.* New Brunswick, N. J. Rutgers University Press. p 1-261.

Chang, M.L.W. and Johnson, M. A. (1980). Effect of Garlic on Carbohydrate Metabolism and Lipid Synthesis in Rats *Journal of Nutrition.* **110:** 931-936.

Chakraborty, D. P., Barman, B. K. and Bose, P. K. (1964). On the structure of girinnimbine, a pyranocarbazole deravative isolated from murraya koeninigi spreng (letters to editor). *Sci.cult.* **20:** 445.

Chakraborty, D. P., Barman, B. K. and Bose, P. K. (1965). On the constitution of murrayanine,a carbazole derivative isolated from Murraya koenigii *Spreng Tetrahedron.* 21: 681.

Chakraborty, D. P. and Das, K. C. (1968). Structure of murrayanine. *J.Org Chem.* 33: 1265.

Chakraborty, D. P., Das , K. C. and Chowdhury, B. K. (1971). structure of murrayacine. *J.Org Chem.* **36**:725.

Chakraborty, D. P., Islam, A., Basak, S.P. and Das, R. (1970).Structure and murrayazolidine: The first Pentacyclic carbazole alkaloid.*ChemInd.*No.**18**: 593.

Chowdhury, B. K. and Chakraborty, D. P. (1971). Mukoiec acid, the first carbozole carbolic acid from a plant source. *Phytochemistry.* **10:** 1967.

Chi, M.S., Koh, E. T. and Stewart, T. J. (1982). Effects of Garlic on Lipid Metabolism in Rats Fed Cholesterol or Lard."*Journal of Nutrition.***112**:41-48.

Chutani, S. K. and Bordia, A. (1981). The Effect of Fried Versus Raw Garlic on Fibrinolytic Activity in Man". *Atherosclerosis.* **38:** 417-421.

Cinatl, J., Morgenstern, B., Bauer, G., Chandra, P. and Rabenau Hand Doerr, H.W. (2003). Glycyrrhizin, an active component of liquorice roots, and replication of SARS-associated coronavirus. *The Lancet.* **361:** 2045-2046.

Clarke, S. (2002). *Essential Chemistry for Safe Aromatotherapy.* Elsevier Science Health Science div. pp. 1-205.

Connell, D. W. (1970). The chemistry of the essential oil and Oleoresin of Ginger. *Flavor Industry* **1:** 677-693.

D'Amelio, F. S. (1999). Botanicals, A phytocosmetic desk reference. *CRC Press, London.* pp. 361.

Davies, K. J. A. (1995).Oxidative stres: the paradox of aerobic life. In: Free radi-cals and oxidative stress: Environment. Drugs and Food Additives.Rice-Evans, C, Halliewell, B, Lunt, G.G. Eds. London:Portland Press. *Biochemical Society Symposium.* **61:**1-31.

De Boer, L. W. V. and Folts, J. D. (1989). Garlic Extract Prevents Acute Platelet Thrombus Formation in Stenosed Canine Coronary Arteries. *American Heart Journal.* **117**:973-975.

Delaisse, J. M., Eeckhout, Y. , Vaes, G. (1986). Inhibition of bone resorption in culture by (+)-catechins. *Biochemical Pharmacology.* **35** :3091-3094.

Dorman, H.J.D., Peltoketo, A., Hiltunen, R. and Tikkanen, M.J. (2003). Characterization of the antioxidant properties of de-odorised aqueous extracts from selected Lamiacea herbs *Food Chemistry.* **83:** 255-262.

Drewitt, P. N., Butterworth, K. R., Springall, C. D.and Moorhouse, S. R. (1993). Plasma levels of Aluminum after tea ingestion in healthy volunteers. *Food and Chemical Toxicology.* **31**: 19-23.

Duke, J. A. (1983). *Medicinal Plants of the Bible, 1ˢᵗ edition, Conch publications, New York* .pp.1-233.

Duke, J. A. (1985). *Handbook of medicinal Herbs. Boca Raton : CRC Press.* pp. 1-677.

Duke, J. A. (1997). *The Green Pharmacy.* Rondale press. PA pp.1-483.

Duke, J. A, Telatnik, M. A. And Duke, P. K. (1999). *Herbs of the Bible.* Interweave Press pp.1-260.

Duke, J. A. (2001). *Dr. Duke's Essential Herbs.* Saint Martin's Press, LLC. pp. 1-254.

Dutt, S. (1958). The Indian Curry leaf tree (Murraya koenigii Spreng.) and its essential oil. *Indian Soap J.* 23: 201.

Elcort, M. (1991). *The Secret Life of Food: A Feast of Food and Drink History, Folklore and Fact.* J. P. Tarcher; 1st Ed. pp.1-185.

Elisabeth, L., (1992). *Encyclopedia of Herbs, Spices, and Flavorings.* D.K. Publishers (T) pp. **1-270.**

Ellen, F. (1997). *The complete book of Spices.* Quinter Publishing Ltd. London, pp.6-127.

Ellis, B. E., and Towers G.H.N.(1970). Biogenesis of rosmarinic acid in mentha. *Biochemistry Journal* **118**: 291-297.

Ernst, E. (1985). Garlic and Blood Lipids. *British Medical Journal* **291**:139.

Escribano, J., Alonso, G. L., Coca-Prados, M. and Fernández, (1996). Crocin, safranal and picocrocin from saffron (*Crocus sativus* L.) inhibit the growth of human cancer cells *in vitro. Cancer Letters* **100:** 23-30.

Evans, P., Hucklebridge, F., Clow, A., Evans, P., Philip, H.F.E. and Angela, C.(2000). *Mind, Immunity and Health: the science of psycho neuro immunology.* London: Free association Press. pp.1-*185.*

Farouk, S. E-F. and Dantel, A. B.(1983). *J Chem Soc Perkin Trans.* **1**: 355.

Fenwick, G. R. and Hanley, A.B. (1986 a). The genus Allium. Critical *Reviews on Food Science.* **22:** 199-271.

Fenwick, G. R. and Hanley, A. B. (1986 b). The genus Allium. Critical *Reviews on Food Science.* **23:** 273-377.

Foster, S. (1999). *A sensible Guide to the Use of Herbs and Related Remedies.* Howorth Press, New York. pp. 1-442.

Fukai, T., Marumo, A., Kaitou, K.; Kanda, T., Terada, S. and Nomura, T. (2002). Anti-*Helicobacter pylori* Flavonoids from licorice extracts. *Life Science.* **71:** 1449-1463.

Fukai, T. Marumo, A. Kaito, K. Kanda, T., Terada, S. and Nomura, T.(2002). Antimicrobial activity of licorice Flavonoids against methicillin-resistant Staphylococcus aureus. *Fitoterapia.* **73:** 536-539.

Fulder, S. (1996). *The Ginger Book: The Ultimate Home Remedy.* Avery Publishing Group. pp. 1-120.

Fulder, S. (1997). *The Garlic Book: The Ultimate Home Remedy.* Avery Publishing Group. pp. 1-100.

Fulder, S. (1998). *Green Tea: The Ultimate Home Remedy.* Avery Publishing Group. pp. 20-106.

Gazzani, G. (1994). Anti and prooxidant activity of some dietary vegetables. *Rivista Scienza dell' Alimentazione.* **23:** 413-420.

Gebhardt, R. (1993). Multiple inhibitory effects of garlic extracts on cholesterol biosynthesis in hepatocytes *Lipids.* **28:** 613-619.

Gilbert, R. M. (1984). Caffeine consumption. *Progress in Clinical and Biological Research.* **158:**185-213.

Goutam, M. P. and Purohit, R.M. (1974) Antimicrbial activity of the essential oil of the leaves of M. koenigii(Linn) Spreng. (Indian Curry leaf) *Indian J Pharm* **36:**11.

Gorden, P., Ferguson , J. H. and Fauci, A. S. (1994). *Helicobacter Pylori* in peptic ulcer disease. *NIH Consensus Statement.* **12** National Institute of health, Bethesda pp 1-23.

Granger, R. and Passet, J. (1973). "*Thymus vulgaris* spontané en France. Races chimiques et chimiotaxonomie." *Phytopharmacie* **12 :** 1683-1691.

Grieve, M. (1972). *Botanicals: A Modern Herbal.* Dover Publications, Inc. New York Vol 1.pp.1-859.

Gujral, S., Bhumura, H. and Swaroop, M. (1978). Effect of Ginger Oleoresin on Serum Cholesterol Levels in Cholesterol Fed Rats. *Nutrition Reports International.* 17: 183-189.

Gupta, G. L. and Nigam, S. S. (1970). Chemical examination of the leaves of Murraya koenigii. *Planta Med.* 19: 83.

Hartwig, S., Rolf, Q. and Hans, K. (2003). Rapid evaluation and quantitative analysis of thyme, oregano and chamomile essential oils by ATP-IR and NIR spectroscopy. *Journal of Molecular Structure, Article in Press.*

He, Y. H. and Kies, C. (1994). Green and Black tea consumption by humans. Impact on polyphenol concentrations in feces, blood and urine. *Plant Foods for Human Nutrition.* 46: 221-229.

Honda, M. and Hara, Y. (1993). Inhibition of rat small intestinal sucrase and alpha-glucosidase activities by tea polyphenols. *Bioscience, Biotechnology and Biochemistry.* 57: 123-124.

Hughes, B. G. and Lawson, L. D. (1991). Antimicrobial Effects of Allium sativum L. (garlic), Allium ampeloprasum (elephant garlic) and Allium cepa (onion), Garlic compounds and Commercial Garlic Supplement Products. *Phytotherapy Research.* 5: 154-158.

Iinuma, M., Ito, T., Miyake, R., Tosa, H. , Tanaka, T. and Chelladurai, V. (1998). A Xanthone from Garcinia Cambogia. *Phytochemistry* 47: 1169-1170.

Iraj, R. and Abyaneh, M. R. (2004) Inhibitory Effects of Thyme oils on growth and Aflatoxin production by *Aspergillus parasiticus. Food Control,* 15: 479-483

Jain, R.C., Vyas, C. R. and Mahtma, O. P. (1973). Hypoglycemic Action of Onions and Garlic. *Lancet.* 2: 1941.

James, E., and Varro, E. (1999). *The Therapeutic use of Phytomedicinals.* Haworth Pr Inc. pp. 1-260.

Jappe, U., Bonnekoh, B., Hausen, B. M. and Gollnick, H. (1999). Garlic-related dermatoses: case report and review of the literature. *Am. J. Contact Dermat.* 10: 37-39.

Jarvis, M. J. (1993). Does caffeine intake enhance absolute levels of cognitive performance? *Psychopharmacology.* **110:** 45-52.

Jeong, H. G. and Kim, J. Y. (2002). Induction of inducible nitric oxide synthase expression by glycyrrhitic acid in macrophages. *FEBS Lett.* **513:** 208-212.

Joshi, B. S, and Kamat,,V. N. and Gawad , D. H. (1969). On the structure of Girinimbine, mahanimbine, Isomahanimbine, Koenimbidine and Murrayacine.*Terahedron.* 26: 1475.

Juliano, C., Mattana, A. and Usai, M. (2000). Composition and in vitro antimicrobial activity of the essential oil of Thymus herba-barona Loisel growing wild in Sardinia. *Journal of Essential Oil Reseach.* **12:** 516-522.

Kaloustian, J., T. F.El-Moselhy and Potugal, H. (2003). Chemical and thermal analysis of the biopolymers in thyme. *Thermochimica Acta.* **401:** 77-86.

Kahneman, D. (1999). Objective happiness. In: *Well-being foundation: the foundation of hedonic psychology* by Kahneman, D., Diener, E., Schwarz, N. *New York: Russell-Sage Foundation* pp. **3-25.**

Kerr, C. (2002). Curry ingredient protects skin against radiation. **The Lancet** *Oncology.* **3:** 713.

Khandare, A. L., Rao, G. S. and Lakshmaiah, N. (2002). Effect of tamarind ingestion on fluoride excretion in humans. *European Journal of Clinical Nutrition.* **56:** 82-85.

Kim, H. M. and Lee, E. H. (1998). Effect of Syzygium aromaticum extract on immediate hypersensitivity in rats. *Journal of Ethnopharmacology* **60:**125-131.

Kishore, N., Dubey, N. K., Tripathi, R. D. and Singh, S. K.(1982). Fungitoxic activity of leaves of some higher plants *Natl Acad Sci. Lett.* **5:** 9.

Kono, S., Shinchi, K. and Ikeda, N.(1992). Green tea consumption and serum lipid profiles: a cross-sectional study in Japan. *Preventive medicine* **21:** 526-531.

Kureel, S. P., Kapil, R.S. and Popli, S. P. (1969). New alkaloids from Murraya koenigii Spreng. *Experientia.* **25:** 790.

Lamarine, R. J. (1994). Selected health and behavioral effects related to the use of caffeine. *Journal of Community Health.* **19**: 449-467.

Lawless, J. (1994).*Lavender oil.* London Thorsons Harper & Collins .pp.1-100

Lawson, L. D. (1993). Bioactive organosulfur compounds of garlic and garlic products: role in reducing blood lipids". In: "Human Medicinal Agents from Plants. by Kinghorn, A. D, Balandrin, M.F *American Chemical Society.* pp. 306-330.

Lee Y., Howard, L. R. and Villalon, B. (1995). Flavonoid and ascorbic acid content and antioxidant activity of fresh pepper cultivators. *IFT Annual Meeting* pp.1-79.

Lee, K. G.and Shibamoto, T. (2001). Antioxidant property of aroma extract isolated from clove bud [Syzygiun aromaticum (L.) Merr. et Perry]. *Food Chem.* **74**: 443–448.

Lee, K. G. and Shibamoto, T. (2001). Inhibition of malonaldehyde formation from blood plasma oxidation by aroma extracts and aroma compounds isolated from clove and eucalyptus. *Food and Chemical Toxicity.* **39**: 1199-1204.

Lee, K.G. and Takayuki, S. (2001).Antioxidant property of aroma Extract isolated from clove buds. *Food Chemistry.* **74**: 443-448.

Leonteva, T. P, Kazakov, A. L. and Ryzhenkov, V. E. (1979). *Voprosy Meditsinkoi Khimii.* **25**: 444-447.

Leoni, E., Tomi, P., Kaloustian, J. and N.Balbi, (2001). 32*emes journées de calorimetries et d'analyse thermique, Hammamet, Tunisia.* Presented paper.

Lewis, Y. S. and Neelakantan, S. (1965). (-)-Hydroxycitric acid- The principal acid in the fruits of *Garcinia cambogia* Desr. *Phytochemistry.* 4 : 619-625.

Lowenstein, J. M. (1971). Effect of (-)-hydroxycitrate on fatty acid synthesis by rat liver *in vivo. J Biol Chem.* **246**: 629-632.

Li, N., Lin, G., Kwan, Y. W. and Min, Z. D. (1999). Simultaneous quantification of five major biologically active ingredients of saffron by high-performance liquid chromatography. *Journal of Chromatography.* **849**: 349-355

Lin, Y. L., Huang, Y. L., Ma, S. H., Yeh, C.T, Chiou, S. Y., Chen, L. K. and Liao, C. L. (1997). Inhibition of Japanese encephalitis virus infection by nitric oxide on RNA virus replication. *J Virol.* **71**: 5227-5235.

Liu, Z., Li, M. and Zhang, G. (1995). An approach to determining the effect on salivary amylase by green tea extract *Chinese Journal of Stomatology.* **30**: 89-91.

Malla, S., Shukala, V. S., Nigam, M. C. and Handa, K.L. (1962). Essential oil of *Mentha avensis*. *Indian oil soap J.* 27: 173.

Masson, D. and Deglise, X. (1982). *Journees d'etudes ADITEC 82, Valorisation des sous-produits et des dechets des industries agro-alimentaires et agricoles, Lyon, France, presented paper*

Matsuda, H., Kagerura, T., Toguchida, I., Ueda, H., Morikawa ,T. and Yoshikawa, M.(2000). Inhibitory effects of sesquiterpenes from bay leaf on nitric oxide production in lipopolysaccharide-activated macrophages: structure requirement and role of heat shock protein induction. *Life Sci.* **66**: 2151.

Mahan, L. K. (2003). *Krause's Food, Nutrition and Diet Therapy* W. B. Saunders Company; 11th Edition. pp. 1-250.

Makimura, M., Hirasawa, M., Kobayashi, K., Indo, J., Sakanaka, S., Taguchi, T. and Otake, S. (1993). Inhibitory effect of tea catechins on collagenase activity. *Journal of Periodontology.* **64**: 630-636.

Mar, C. and Bent, S. (1999). An evidence-based review of the most commonly used herbs. *WMJ* **171**: 168-171.

Marathe, R. M., Annapure, U. S., Singhal, R. S.and Kulkarni, P. R. (2002). Gelling behaviour of polyose from tamarind kernel polysaccharide. *Food Hydrocolloids.* **16**: 423-426.

Marshall, B. J and Warren, J. R. (1984). Unidentified curved bacilli in the stomach of patients with gastritis and peptic ulceration. *The Lancet.* pp. 1311-1315.

Martini, H., Weidenbörner, M., Adams, S. and Kunz, B. (1996). Eugenol and Carvacrol: The Main Fungicidal Compounds in Clove and Savory. *Ital. J. Food Sci.* 1: 63 - 67.

Matsumoto, N., Ishigaki, F., Ishigaki, A., Iwashina, H. and Hard, Y. (1993). "Reduction of Blood glucose levels by tea catechins." *Bioscience, Biotechnology and Biochemistry*. **57**: 525-527.

Maarit, O., Peltoketo, A. Hartonen, K., *et al.*, (2002). Extraction of sage by pressurized hot water and conventional methods: antioxidant activity of the extracts. *European Food Research and Technology*. **215**: 158-163.

Marry, M., Cavalier, D. M. , Schnurr, J. K. , Netland, J., Yang, Z, Pezeshk, V., York, W. S., Pauly, M. and White, A. R. (2003). Structural characterization of chemically and enzymatically derived standard oligosaccharides isolated from partially purified tamarind xyloglucan. *Carbohydrate Polymers* **51**: 347-356.

McKenna, D. J, Jones, K. and Hughes, K. (2001). Efficacy, Safety and Use of Gingko Biloba in clinical and preclinical applications. *Altern. Ther. Health Med*. **7**: 70-90.

Mitamura, T., Kitazono, M., Yoshimura, O. and Yakushiji, M. (1989). The influence of Green Tea upon the improvement of Iron deficiency anemia with pregnancy treated by Sodium Ferrous Citrate. *Acta Obstetrica et Gynaecologica*. **41**: 688-694.

Mitscher L. A. and Dolby Victoria. (1998). *The Green Tea Book* Avery Publishing Group. 1-140.

Morris, N. (2002). The effects of lavender baths on psychological well-being: two exploratory randomized control trials. *Complementary Therapies in Medicine*. **10**:223-228.

Morton, J. (1987). *Fruits of warm Climates. Creative resources systems*. **pp.**115-121.

Mowrey, D. B. and D. E. Claysion. (1982). Motion Sickness, Ginger and Psychophysics. *Lancet*. **1**: 655-657.

Mustafa, T. and Srivastava, K. C. (1990). Ginger in Migraine Headaches. *Journal of Ethnopharmacology*. **29**: 267-273.

Nair, S. K. K. and Hasegawa, J. H. (1995). Saffron chemoprevention in biology and medicine: a review. *Cancer Biotherapy*. **10**: 257-264.

Narasimhan, N. S., Paradkar, M.V. and Chitguppi, V. P. (1968). Structure of Mahanimbin and koenimbin. *Tetrahedron Lett. No*. **53**: 5501.

Nayak, K. P. and Dutta, N. K. (1961). Role of essential oils and allied drugs in experimental cholera of the rabbit. *Indian J. Med Res*.**49:** 59.

Nigam, S. S. and Purohit, R. M., (1961). Chemical examination of the essential oil derived from the leaves of Murrya koenigii (Linn) Sreng.(Indian Curry leaf).*Perfume Essent oil Rec*. **52:** 152.

Nomura, T. and Fukai, T. (1998). Phenolic constituents of licorice. *Progress in the chemistry of organic natural products*. **73:** 1-140.

Norman, J. (1991). *The Complete Book of Spices*. Viking Press.pp. 1-120

Ohmori, Y., Ito, M., Kishi, M., Mizutani, H., Katada, T. and Konishi, H. (1995). Antiallergic constituents from oolong tea stem. *Biological and Pharmaceutical Bulletin*. **18:** 683-686.

Ooshima ,T., Minami, T., Aono, W., *et al* (1993). Oolong tea polyphenols inhibit experimental dental caries in SPF rats infected with mutans streptococci. *Caries Research* **27(2):** 124-129.

Parnham, M. J. and Kesselring, K., (1985). Rosmarinic acid. *Drugs of the Future* **10:** 756-757.

Peterson., M. and Simmonds, M. S. J. (2000). Rosmarinic Acid. *Phyto chemistry* **62:** 121-125.

Penny, M. K.E., Hecker, K. D, Bonanome, A., Coval, S. M., Binkoski, A. E , Hilpert, K, F , Griel, A. E. and Etherton, T. D. (2002). Bioactive compounds in foods: their role in the prevention of cardiovascular disease and cancer. *The American Journal of Medicine*. **113:** 71-88.

Peter, K.V. (2001). *Handbook of herbs and spices*. Woodhead Publishing. **20-360.**

Pokorny, J. (1991). Natural antioxidants for food use. *Trends Food Sci. Technol*. **2:** 223-227.

Popenoe, W. (1974). *Manual of Tropical and Subtropical Fruits*. *Hafner Press* pp. 432-436.

Potter, N. and Hotchkiss, J. (1995). *Food Science*. Kluwer Academic Publishers.pp.100-126.

Rattan, S. I. (1988). Science behind the spices: Inhibition of Platelet Aggregation and Prostaglandin Synthesis. *Bioassays*. **8:** 161-162.

Reiter, M. and Brandt, W. (1985). *Arzneimittelforschung.* **35**: 408-414.

Rosengarten, F. Jr. (1969). *The book of spices.* Wynnewood, PA, Livingston Pub: pp.1-130.

Roy, S. and Chakraborty, D. P. (1974). Mahanimbine from Murraya koenigii Spreng.*Phytochemistry.***13**: 2893.

Roy, S., Gosh, S. and Chakraborty, D. P. (1979). Structure of Mahanimboline *Chem Ind.no.* **14**: 669.

Roy, S., Bhattacharya, L. and Chakraborty, D. P. (1982). Structure and synthesis of mukoline and mukolidine; two new carbazole alkaloids from Murraya koenigii Spreng. *J. Indian Chem Soc.***59**: 1369.

Sagesaka-Mitane, Y., Miwa, M. and Okada, S. (1990). Platelet Aggregation inhibitors in hot water extract of green tea. *Chemical and Pharmaceutical Bulletin.* **38**: 790-793.

Sainani, G. S., Desai, D. B., Gorhe, N. H., Natu, S. M., Pise, D.V.and Sainani, P.G. (1979). Effect of Dietary Garlic and Onion on Serum Lipid Profile in a Jain Community. *Indian Journal of Medical Research.* **69**: 776-780.

Sato, T., and Niwa, M. (1995). Cariostatic mechanisms of fluoride and its effects on human beings. *Japanese Journal of Clinical Medicine.* **54**:568-572.

Satyavati, G. V, Raina, M. K. and Sharma, M. (1976). Medicinal Plants of India . *Indian council Of Medical Research N. Delhi.* Vol.1.pp.1-486.

Satyavati, G. V, Gupta, A. K. and Tandon, N. (1987). Medicinal   Plants of India . *Indian council OfMedical Research N. Delhi.* Vol.2.pp. 21-554.

Scarpati, M. L. and Oriente, G. (1958). Isolamento e costituzione dell'acido rosmarinico. *Ric. Sci.* **28**: 2329-2333.

Schilcher, H. (1973). Recent Knowledge in quality evaluation of Chamomile bloosoms respectively chamomile oil.2.Quality evaluation of the volatile oil in Flores Chamomillae Grading of Commercial chamomiles into 4 respectively 5 chemical types. *Planta Med.* **23**:132.

Schultz, V., Hansel, R. and Tyler, V. E. (1998). *Rational phytotherapy: A physician's guide to herbal medicine.* New York Springer- v_Verlag Telos; 3rd Ed.pp.1-306.

Shafran, I. (1976). Nutmeg toxicity. *N. Engl. J. Med.* **294:** 849.

Shahidi, F., Janitha, P. K. and Wanasundara, P. D. (1992). Phenolic antioxidants. *Critical reviews in Food Science and Nutrition* **32:** 67-103.

Shibata, S. and Saitoh, T. (1973). The chemical constituents of licorice roots. *Taisha.* **10:** 619-625.

Shibata, S. (2000). A drug over the millennia: pharmacognosy, chemistry, and pharmacology of licorice. Yakugaku Zasshi. **120:** 849-862.

Shoji, N., Iwasa A., Takemoto, T., Ishida, Y. and Ohizumi, Y. (1982). Cardiotonic principles of Ginger. *Journal of Pharmaceutical Sciences.* **71:** 1174-1175.

Smith, M. (2003). The psychological effects of lavender in literature and plays. *International Journal of Aromatotherapy.* **13:** 18-22.

Sunter, W. H. (1999). Warfarin and garlic. *Pharmaceutical journal.* **246:** 722.

Sollman, T. (1957). In: A manual of Pharmacology and its Applications to Therapeutics and toxicology. Sollaman,T. H. 8th.Ed W. B. Saunders Co. Philadelphia, pp.192-193.

Shobana, S. and Akhilender Naidu, K., (2000). Antioxidant Activity of Selected Indian Spices. *Prostaglandins, Leukotrienes and Essential Fatty Acids.* **62:** 107-110.

Sullivan, A. C., Hamilton, J.G., Miller, O. N. and Wheatley, V. R. (1972). Inhibition of Lipogenesis in Rat Liver by (-) - Hydroxycitrate *Archives of Biochemistry and biophysics.* **150:** 183-190.

Sullivan, A. C., Triscari, J., Hamilton, G., and Miller, O.N., (1974). Effect of (-)-hydroxycitrate upon accumulation of lipid in the rat: II. Appetite *Lipids* **9:** 129 – 134.

Sullivan, A. C., Triscari, J. and Spiegel, J. E. (1977). Metabolic regulation as a control for lipid disorder. II. Influence of (-)-hydroxycitrate on genetically and experimentally induced hypertriglyceridemia in the rat. *Am J Clin Nutr.* **30:** 777-84.

Takagi, K. and Ishii, Y. (1967). Peptic ulcer inhibiting properties of a new fraction from licorice root. Experimental peptic ulcer and general pharmacology. *Arzneimittel-Forschung* **17:** 1544- 547.

Takahashi, T. (1981). Warm rain study in Hawaii-Raininitiation. *J. Atmos. Sc.* **38**: 347-369.

Takayanagi, T., Ishikawa, T. and Kitajima, J. (2003). Sesquiterpene lactone glucosides and alkyl glycosides from the fruit of cumin. *Phytochemistry* **63**: 479-484.

Takikawa, A. (2002). Antimicrobial activity of Nutmeg against E. coli O157. *Journal of Bioscience and Bioengineering.* **94**: 315-320.

Tesch, B. J. (2003): Herbs commonly used by women: An evidence-based review. *Am J Obstet Gynecol.* **188**: S44-S55.

Terada , A., Hara, H., Nakajayo, S., *et al.*, (1993). Effect of supplements of tea polyphenols on the caecal flora and ceacal metabolites of chicks. *Microbial Ecology in Health and Disease.* **6**: 3-9.

Visudhiphan, S., Poolsuppasit, S. , Piboonnukarintr, O. and Tumliang, S. (1982). The relationship between high fibrinolytic activity and daily capsicum ingestion in Thais. *American Journal of Clinical Nutrition.* **35**: 1452-1458.

Vogl, T. P. (1982). Treatment of Human Hand. *New England Journal of Medicine* **306**: 178.

Veluraja, K. Ayyalnarayanasubburaj, S. and Paulraj, A. J. (1997). Preparation of gum from Tamarind seed- and its application in the preparation of composite material with sisal fiber. *Carbohydrate Polymers.* **34**: 377-379.

Vrinda, K. and. Garg, S. R (2001). Inhibitory effect of clove oil on Listeria monocytogenes in meat and cheese. *Food Microbiology.* **18**: 647-650.

Warrier, P. K., Nambiar, V. P. K. and Ramankutty, C. 1994). *Indian Medicinal Plants a compendium of 500 species.* Vol.1. Orient Longman Pvt. Ltd. Madras India. pp.1-420.

Warrier, P. K., Nambiar, V. P. K. and Ramankutty, C. 1994). *Indian MedicinalPlants a compendium of 500 species.* Vol.2.Orient Longman Pvt. Ltd. Madras India. pp.1-416.

Warrier, P. K., Nambiar, V. P. K. and Ramankutty, C. (1995). *Indian Medicinal Plants a compendium of 500 species.* Vol.3. Orient Longman Pvt. limited Madras India.pp.1-423.

Warrier, P. K., Nambiar, V. P. K. and Ramankutty, C. (1995). *Indian Medicinal Plants a compendium of 500 species.* Vol.4.Orient Longman Pvt. limited Madras India.pp.1-444.

Warrier, P. K., Nambiar, V. P. K. and Ramankutty, C. (1996). *Indian Medicinal Plants a compendium of 500 species.* Vol.5. Orient Longman Pvt. limited Madras India.pp.1-592.

Watson, J. A. and Lowenstein, J. M. (1970). Citrate and the conversion of carbohydrate into fat. Fatty acid synthesis by a combination of cytoplasm and mitochondria. *J Biol Chem.* **245:** 5993.

Wada, K., Ueda, N., Sawada, H., Amemiya, N. and Haga, M. (1997). Inductive effects of bay leaf and its component costunolide on the mouse liver glutathione S-transferase. *Natural Medicines.* **51:** 283.

Wagovich, M. J. (1987). Diallyl Sulphide, a Flavor Component of Garlic, Inhibits Dimethylhydrazine Induced Colon Cancer. *Carcinogenesis.* **8:** 487-489.

Warshafsky, S., Kamer, R. S. and Sivak, S. L. (1993). Effect of Garlic on Total Serum Cholesterol: a Meta-Analysis. *Annals of Internal Medicine.* **119:** 599-605.

Weisberger, H. S. and Pensky, J. (1957). Tumor-Inhibiting Effects Derived from an Active Principle of Garlic. *Science.* **126:** 1112-1114.

Willatgamuwa, S. A., Platel, M.S. K. *et al.* (1998). Antidiabetic influence of Dietary cumin seeds (Cuminum cyminum) in streptozotocin induced diabetic rats. *Nutrition Research.* **18:** 131-142.

Yoshikawa, M., Shimoda, H., Uemura, T., Morikawa, T., Kawahara, Y. and Matsuda, H. (2000). Alcohol absorption inhibitors from bay leaves: structure-requirements of sesquiterpenes for the activity. *Bioorganic and medicinal chemistry.* **8:** 2071-2077.

Zheng, G. Q., Kenney, P. M. and Lam, L. K. (1992). Sesquiterpenes from clove as potential anticarcinogenic agents. *Journal of Natural Products.* **55:** 999-1003.

Zheng, W., Doyle, T. J., Kushi, L. H., Sellers, T. A., Hong, C. P. and Felsom, A. B. (1992). Tea consumption and cancer incidence in a prospective cohort study of postmenopausal women. *American Journal of Epidemiology.* **166:** 475-477.

Book Indexing

Acrid, 113
Aflatoxin, 93
Ailments, 103
Ajowan, 94,95
Allergic, 75,105
Allergy, 4,8,31
Allicin, 40,61
Allium, 39, 58
*Allium cepa,*59
Allium sativum, 39
Alternaria, 3
Alzheimer's disease, 51,109
Amenorrhea, 45,111
Analgesic, 46, 102
Anethole, 2, 3, 4
Anethum, 36
Anethum graveolens, 36
Angina , 45
Anis, 1
Anise oil, 2
Aniseed, 1
Anisum vulgare, 1
Anodyne, 73
Anthelmintic, 26,30 ,72,75,100,103,105, 107,111,113
Antherosclerosis, 46
Anti- HIV activity, 57
Anti inflammatory, 30,72,74,102,105,113
Antiaging, 93
Antiarthrits, 74
Antibacterial, 3,8,21,34,38,75,83,100,109,111
Anticarcinogenic, 26,42
Anticonvulsive,12,46
Anti- edemic, 75
Antifungal, 3,7,34 ,40 ,72,89,111
Antimicrobial, 7 ,26,30 ,40,46,57, 81,93
Antimutagen, 65
Antimutagenic, 74,77
Antioxidant, 3 ,11,26,27,35,46, 47,57,65, 75,77

Antiprotozoa, 35,111
Antipyretic,105
Antiseptic, 2,40 ,49 ,72,83,103,111
Antispasmodic, 24,30,35,46,72,102
Antitumor, 46,72
Antiviral, 64,81,83,111
Aphrodisiac, 4,19, 54,62,68,72,97,107,119
Apiaceae, 1
Apium, 1
Appetizer, 75
Arabic kaak, 2
Aromatic, 3
Arteriosclerosis, 27,46,47,77,79
Arthritis, 45,65,100
Aspergillus, 3 ,22,34,93,
Asthmatic /Asthma, 19,30 ,38,41,54,57,72,75 100,111 ,113
Astringent, 49 ,54, 72,105,109
Atherosclerosis, 51
*Bacillus subtillis,*46
Bactericide, 26
Baldness, 65
Balsamic, 68
Basil, 98, 99
Bay leaf, 5
Bitter, 114
Black pepper,9
Blood pressure, 40
Boils, 72
Bonchitis, 30, 75, 111
Brassica alba, 112
Brassica campestris, 112
Brassica nigra, 112
Brassica, 112,
Calming, 89
Cambodge , 48
Camellia sinensis 76,77
Cancer, 65.
Candida , 22, 34
Capsaicin, 14

Capsicum, 13,14
Capsicum annum, 13
Caram ajowan, 95,96
Caraway seed, 94, 96 ,97
Carcinogen, 81
Cardamom, 17,18
Cardamomum, 17
Cardiotonic , 68,100
Carminative,3,30,34,38,40,46 ,54,69 ,75, 102,105,107,109,111,113
Carum carvi, 95, 96, 97
Catarrh, 19
Cathartic, 73
Cataracts, 45
Chamomile, 101,102,103.
Choleretic, 75,
Cholesterol, 15 ,40 , 42 ,47, 50, 68, 79, 80
Cinnamomum zeylanicum, 20
Cinnamon, 20
Citric acid, 71
Cladosporium, 3
Clove, 24
Clostridium, 8,11
Clotting ,15
Colds, 100
Colic, 12 ,38,36 ,40,75,97,111.
Colletotrichum, 34
Conjunctivitis, 72
Constipation, 12,40,104
Convulsions, 103
Coriander,105
Coriandrum sativum, 105
Corynebactreium, 3 ,34
Cosmetic, 2
Cramps, 64,97,102,105
Crocus sativus, 68
Culinary, 2
Cumin, 28
Cuminum cyminum, 28
Curcuma, 73
Curcuma domestica, 73
Curcumene, 45

Curry leaf, 32
Dairy cattle, 3
Dandruff, 66
Diaphoretic, 69
Demulcent, 49
Depression, 89
Depressor effect, 77
Dermatitis, 4, 27
Dermatophyte, 89
Diabetes, 22,27,75
Diarrhea, 12 ,30 66,72,105
Dill, 36, 37
Diuretic, 8,30,38,61,75,79,84,100,103,105, 107
Dizzycorn, 104
Dropsy, 103
Dysentery, 22,35,51, 63,101,106
Dyspepsia, 75
Ecbolic, 69
Eczema, 57
Edema, 22
Egenol, 6, 21,27,53
Elephantiasis, 47,75
Emetic, 8, 113
Emmenagougue, 8, 69
Emollient, 49,110
Emphysema, 19
Entamoeba histolytica 35
Epilepsy,75
Epistaxis, 105
Erythema, 4
Escherichia coli , 22, 46.
Expectorant,19,61,69,75,83,100,103,105,107, 111
Facial paralysis, 41
Fainting, 65
Febrifuge, 35,72,103
Fennel,. 106,107
Foeniculum vulgare, 106
Fenugreek,108 ,109
Trigonella foenum-graecum, 108
Fever 30,75,100, 108, 111
Flatulence, 30,35,38,40,75,100,105, 111,113

Flavonoids, 83,92,97,107
Flu, 22 ,46,66,100
Fusarium, 3
Galatagogue, 107
Garcinia, 48
Garcinia cambogia, 48
Garcinia indica, 48
Garlic, 39
Gastric ulcer, 84
Giddiness, 75,100
Ginger,44
Gingivitis ,72
Glucosuria , 30
Glycyrrhiza glabra, 82
Glycyrrhiza, 83
Gonorrhea,30
Green tea, 76,77,78,79,80,81
Hallucinations, 54
Helicobacter pylori, 84
Helminthiasis, 35,54
Hemorrhages, 100
Hemorrhoids,30,38,41,62,79,84,100,103
105,107
Hepatic regeneration, 3
Hepatotoxin, 4
Herpes, 16
Hiccups, 22 ,113
Hperglycemia, 30
Hpoglycemic properties, 7
Hypertensin, 79
Hypotensive, 75
Hysteria,6, 41,103
Immune deficiency, 27
Impotency, 54
Inflammation, 12,105,107
Insecticidal ,100
Insectiside, 12
Insomania, 54
Insomanic, 102
Iron absorption, 3
Itching, 31
Jaundice, 62,75,103
Kokaum, 48

Lactation,12
Larus nobilis, 5
Laryngitis,51
Lavandula officinalis, 86
Lavender, 87,88
Laxative, 76
Leprosy, 30,35, 41,75
Leucoderma,35, 62,100
Libido, 3,18
Licorice, 82,83,84,85
Leucorrhea, 30
Lumbago, 41 ,63
Malarial fever, 62 ,100
Marjoram, 55,56,57
*Matricaria chamomilla,*102
Menopause,107
Medical, 2,6
Menstruation,/Menstrual,3 ,45,57 ,64,66,100,
106,107,108
Menthae piperitae, 110,111
Mint, 110
Microsporum gypseum, 34
Migraines , 7,64
Milk flow, 66
Milk secretion, 97
Morning sickness, 46
Motion sickness, 46
Mouth wash, 4
Mukoeic acid, 33
Murraya koenigii, 32,33,34,35
Mustard,.112
Mycobacterium, 46
*Myristica fragrans,*52
Narcotic, 54
Nausea, 4,31,46,78
Nervine, 70
Neuralgia,103,105
Nightmares, 2
Nut meg and Mace, 52, 54
Ocimum basilicum, 98,99
Ocimum scantum, 99
Oestragole, 98
Oestrogenic/ Oestrogen, 2,3

Oleoresin, 10,14,15
Olestrin, 11
Oligosacchrides, 71
Onion, 58,59,60,61,62
Opthalmia, 79 ,100
Oregano, 55,56,57
Origanum majorana, 55
Origanum vulgare, 55
Otalgia, 72
Ophthalmopathy, 30
Parasite, 3
Pasturella multocida, 34
Penicellium, 3
Peptic ulcer, 83,84,111
Perfumery/ Perfumes, 2, 6
Pestisides, 7
Pimpenella anisum ,1
Pepper, 9 ,10,11,12
Piper nigrum, 9
Platelet activation, 40
Polyphenols, 79, 80
Poultice, 113
Pruritus, 75,100
Pseudomonas, 11, 22
Pudina, 110
Refrigerant, 72
Religious importance, 2, 6
Restore youth, 2
Rheumatism, 48,54,103
Rhizoctonia solani, 35
Ring worm, 72,75 ,100
Rosmaric acid, 63
Rosmarinus officianalis, 63
Rosmary, 63,64,65
Rutaceae, 32
Sacchromyces cerivisiae, 22
Saffron, 67, 68,69
Safrole, 53
Sage, 63 ,65, 66
Salmonella, 3 , 7
Salvia, 65
SARS- associated virus, 85

Scabies, 72
Scaling, 4
Shigella flexnerii, 7
Sciatica, 41
Seborrhea, 45
Shingles, 16
Smallpox , 73,109
Sore throat, 46 ,67
Spasmolytic, 3
Splenomegaly, 113
Staphylococus aureus, 3,7,11, 22, 34
Stimulant, 61,69,100
Stomachic, 8,15,32,,54,75,105, 111
Streptococcus pyrogens, 3
Sudorific , 8
Sweet cumin, 1
Syphilis, 38
Syzygium aromaticum, 24
Tamarind, 70,71,72
Tamarindus indica, 70
Tannins, 64, 98
Tendonitis, 45
Thermogenic, 113
Thrombosis, 40
Thyme, 90,91,92,93
Thymus capitatus, 90
Thymus vulgaris, 90
Tonic, 102
Trigonella foenum, 108
Trigonella foenum graecum, 108
Tuberculosis, 41
Turmeric, 73,74, 75
Ulcers, 75,100
Umbelliferone, 2
Vibrio cholerae, 11
Vinegar, 16, 37
Vodka, 2
Vomiting, 4, 31,38,54,105 ,109
Wrinkles, 65
Zingeber officinale, 44
Zingiberaceae, 44,74
Zingiberene, 45